3065

by WINIFRED G. HAMMOND

Illustrated with Photographs

Coward-McCann, Inc.
New York

Plants, Food and People

To the memory of my mother, Mrs. Eva A. Graham,
who loved books from early childhood to old age

Photographs courtesy of:
Allis-Chalmers Mfg. Co., title pages, pages 146, 148
J. I. Case Co., page 140
Denver Museum of Natural History, page 37
FAO, pages 51 (left), 112-113, 118, 119, 122, 125, 129
Ginn & Co. (from Ancient Times by Breasted), page 132
Holt Bros., page 141
International Harvester Co., page 149
Merck & Co., Inc., pages 95, 96
NASA, pages 153, 155, 156
Oriental Institute, University of Chicago, pages 68-69, 70
Robert H. Lowie Museum of Anthropology, University of California, Berkeley,
    pages 43, 45, 51 (right), 84
Southwest Museum, Los Angeles, pages 35, 36
Smithsonian Institution, Bureau of American Ethnology, page 56
United Nations, pages 108, 109
U. S. Department of Agriculture, pages 82 (middle and bottom), 150; Western
    Utilization Res. & Del. Div., page 100
U. S. Department of the Interior, Fish and Wildlife Service, page 62
U. S. Forest Service, pages 19, 20, 21, 23
U. S. Navy official photograph, page 101
University of California, page 14 (top left); Herbarium, Berkeley, and Dept. of
Agronomy, College of Agriculture, Davis, page 82 (top); Sanitary Engineering
    Research Laboratory, pages 14 (top right), 15

092013

Library of Congress Catalog Card Number: 63-15542

MANUFACTURED IN THE UNITED STATES OF AMERICA

Third Impression

CONTENTS

Acknowledgements

I want to express my appreciation to all the people who helped me in the gathering of the material for this book, and to those who supplied the specimens of corn: Miss Annetta Carter, Principal Herbarium Botanist, University of California, Berkeley, and Mr. Dale G. Smeltzer, Lecturer in Agronomy, University of California, College of Agriculture, Davis.

I am particularly grateful to those specialists who read one or more chapters of the manuscript: to Mr. Wayne W. Austin, Washington Field Specialist, Soil Conservation Service, U. S. D. A.; Dr. H. G. Baker, Professor of Botany and Director of the Botanical Garden, University of California, Berkeley; Dr. J. S. Bassham, Associate Director, Bio-Organic Chemistry Group, Lawrence Radiation Laboratory, University of California, Berkeley; Dr. Robert J. Braidwood, Professor of Anthropology, University of Chicago; Dr. Ralph W. Chaney, Professor of Paleontology, Emeritus, of the University of California, Berkeley; Mr. A. B. Elsasser, Graduate Research Archaeologist, R. H. Lowie Museum of Anthropology, University of California, Berkeley; Dr. Robert Heizer, Professor of Anthropology, University of California, Berkeley; Mr. John Lemberger, Naturalist, Wild Life Nurseries, Oshkosh, Wisconsin; Dr. Agnes Fay Morgan, Professor of Nutrition, Emeritus, University of California, Berkeley; Mrs. William Fox, Librarian in the Agriculture Reference Library, University of California, Berkeley; Dr. James W. Pence, Chief of Cereals Laboratory, U. S. Dept. of Agriculture, Western Regional Research Laboratory, Albany, California; Mrs. Myra Perez Navarro, formerly of Ceylon; Mrs. Eleanor Taylor, Technical Editor, Western Regional Research Laboratory; and Dr. Paul Weatherwax, Professor of Botany, Emeritus, University of Indiana, Bloomington.

WINIFRED G. HAMMOND
Berkeley, California

CHAPTER 1

MAN AND PLANTS

Mankind has always been dependent on plants. Primitive man used them for many things: for food, for shelter and for fire. Sometimes he could get along without the last two, but always he had to have the first: food.

Early peoples probably needed about the same amount of food that we do today. In those ancient days certainly there were people who couldn't get enough to satisfy their hunger. Today, in spite of all our gadgets and our technology, there are still hungry people in many parts of the world.

Lord John Boyd Orr, who was the first director of the Food and Agriculture Organization of the United Nations (FAO), said that a lifetime of poor nutrition and actual hunger is the fate of at least two-thirds of the world's population.

In the early days of man, the hunt for food was carried on almost every day by every member of the family except the very young and the very old. Also it took much time to prepare the food — to shell and pound the seeds, strip and boil the roots, skin and cook the animals. The rest of the time was spent in making weapons for the hunt, nets to catch the fish, and baskets or containers in which to collect the seeds and roots.

Scientists call these peoples *hunters and gatherers*. They did not raise any animals; they only killed the wild ones in the woods and plains. Neither did they plant any seeds; they only picked the seeds and nuts of the wild plants.

Although this way of life seems strange to us today, scientists have found that man lived as a hunter-gatherer much longer than he has lived by farming and animal raising.

If, for instance, we could squeeze the five hundred thousand years that man has been on earth into fifty years, we would find that man lived as a hunter-gatherer for forty-nine of those years.

A year ago, in our compressed time, something very important happened. A few people learned to plant seeds that would grow into crops. These crops produced enough food so that the people could stay in one place instead of being always on the move in the search for wild foods. This was such a great step forward that scientists speak of it as the *first agricultural revolution*.

Later, in that last year of compressed time, farmers and stock-raisers learned how to raise enough food so that they could feed not only themselves and their families but a few extra people as well. These other people could then do some other kind of work besides food-getting. They could build houses and temples. They could paint pictures and carve statues. They could study the stars and make calendars.

Early man ate nearly everything he could find that wasn't poisonous. He liked meat — as so many people do today — and ate it whenever he could. His wife and children collected leaves, seeds, roots and berries to add variety to the menu and to keep away hunger when there was no meat. One tribe of Indians, the Shoshones, for example, used *one hundred different kinds of plants*.

When men settled in villages, they couldn't raise this many kinds of plants. Instead, they selected a few that were tasty and would give a sure source of food in quantity. Also these had to be plants that grew well in the areas where the people were living.

Partly as a result of this increased amount of food, great civilizations grew up. Each of these was dependent on the food from a few plants that man had learned to raise in big quantities. Also it had to be a food that wouldn't spoil right away. It had to last until the next year's crop could be planted and reaped.

Out of all the plants in the world the grasses, or grains, were found to satisfy these requirements best for most of the world. The great civilizations of Egypt and the Middle East were based on wheat farming. Many people of Asia found that rice best fitted their need for a plant that grew in the monsoon country of alternating droughts and heavy rains. North and South America had no wild wheat or rice, so the peoples of the Americas developed the corn plant from some — still unknown — wild ancestor.

In some tropical parts of South America where the corn plant did not grow, the ancient peoples cultivated a root food — the manioc — which sustained and nourished them. In the islands of the Pacific the sweet potato and the roots of the taro plant became the people's "bread."

The peoples of the world are still dependent on these same plants which were used by our ancient ancestors. Recent man, in spite of all his scientific advances, has not found a single valuable plant food which was not first used by primitive man. Also in many parts of the world these plants are still raised in much the same way as they were by our stone-age ancestors. The blades of the tools used in farming may have changed from stone and wood to metal, but the shapes and the kinds of tools are much the same.

In other parts of the world, particularly in Northern Europe, the United States, Canada, Australia and Russia, something has happened to farming in the last 100 years. It has made such a great change in farming methods and conditions that scientists call it the *second agricultural revolution*.

If your grandparents lived on a farm they took part in this second great revolution. Perhaps your parents, too, may have been part of this great changeover in farming methods.

This second agricultural revolution has had as great an impact on civilization as did the first one. In fact, we could not live the life we do today with our modern technology if this had not occurred.

Major corn, rice and wheat producing areas in the United States

Scientists have been able to read about and to observe this second revolution. The first one took place so long ago that there are no written records. Scientists called archaeologists employ other methods to "read" this story. Like detectives they go from one small clue to another. The clues to the life of these early peoples are found in caves and in towns long ago buried by soil and trash. The archaeologists dig into these sites and piece together the stories.

Other scientists study primitive peoples still found in the world today, because the scientists say that these people probably live much as their ancestors did.

In this book we shall talk about some of these detective stories and about the great changes that took place in the first and second agricultural revolutions. We shall also discuss briefly man's great dependence on plants from the time of the first man up to the present, and on into the space age when space travelers will be just as dependent on plants as we are.

How do scientists know about this dependence? It has been the subject of a great amount of scientific research, as you will read in the next chapter.

10

CHAPTER 2

PLANTS AND THEIR SUN TRAPS—PHOTOSYNTHESIS

Early man knew he needed plants for shelter, for his fires, and for much of his food. He had no idea how the food that sustained him was made by the plants. Neither did he realize that he was dependent on plants in another way which was just as important to him.

The first hint of this other use came in 1775. In that year Joseph Priestley, an English minister interested in natural science, published the results of his experiments with gases. He didn't call them gases, but different kinds of "air."

Priestley said he could drive air out of many substances. In his experiments he put a small piece of solid substance into the bottom of a thin-walled bottle. (The shape of the bottle was something like the glass lining of a modern vacuum bottle.) He filled the bottle with the silvery liquid, mercury, and turned it upside down in a dish of mercury. Thus, the bottle of mercury was standing bottom-up in the dish with the pieces of solid floating in the mercury just under the glass.

(You can see how this is done by trying it yourself with water. Drop a small piece of cork into a bottle. Then fill the bottle with water, put your finger over the mouth and turn the bottle upside down in a pan of water. As you probably know, the air pressure will keep the water from running out of the bottle as long as its mouth is under the water. Where is the small piece of cork now? Is it floating at the top of the water just under the glass?)

Priestley set up his experiment and then brought out his large magnifying glass, twelve inches across. With this glass he focused a spot of sunlight on the small piece of solid that was just under the glass bottom of his bottle. Of course, the solid became hot. Usually, as it became hot it gave off a gas. This gas would push the mercury part way down in the bottle.

"The solid material expels air," Priestley said.

(You can push the water down in your experiment by blowing air into the mouth of your bottle with a bent soda straw. Be sure you keep the mouth of the bottle under the water the whole time.)

Priestley did experiments with many different solid substances and noted that the air expelled was not always the same kind.

He put in pieces of "mercurius calcinatus," which we know as *mercuric oxide*, a compound of mercury and oxygen. He got about four times as much air as the amount of solid oxide he had put in. Since nobody knew anything about oxygen at this time he didn't realize what he had produced. He was amazed when he put a lighted candle into his air, which was really oxygen.

"What surprised me more than I can well express," he said, "was that a candle burned in this air with a remarkably vigorous flame."

Priestley called his new gas "dephlogisticated air," because even he realized it was different from ordinary air. He did hundreds of experiments with his bottles and his burning-glass. You can read about them in a book he wrote, entitled *Experiments and Observations on Different Kinds of Air*.

In one of Priestley's experiments he put a mouse in a closed jar until — as he said — "it had spoilt the air." In other words, the mouse had used all the oxygen in the air and then had died of suffocation. Next he put a living plant into this same jar where the mouse had died. He was careful not to let any fresh air into the bottle. He left the plant there for some time and then took it out. Now he found that another mouse could live in the air, just as well as if it hadn't been spoiled by the first mouse.

12

Fourteen years later the Dutch physician, Jan Ingenhousz, did many experiments with plants and oxygen, or as he still called it, dephlogisticated air. In one experiment he put plants and cold spring water in a large bottle. He turned the bottle upside down in a tub of the same kind of cold water. He found that when the sun shone on the plants in the jar, bubbles of dephlogisticated air (oxygen) came from the leaves. When there was no sun the bubbles stopped coming.

He concluded, "The light of the sun alone is capable of producing in the leaves that activity which may produce dephlogisticated air."

This was the first statement of the ability of green plants to produce oxygen when light falls on them. After these experiments people began to realize that the green plants of the earth had been replacing the oxygen used by animals for many million years. Thus, man had been using plants in a very important way even though he didn't know it.

Since the time of Priestley and Ingenhousz many scientists have studied this ability of green leaves to give off oxygen when light falls on them. They call this process *photosynthesis*, which means manufacturing with light. Scientists point out that not only do plants manufacture oxygen but in the same process they trap energy from the sun.

If it were not for this photosynthesis, life on this earth as we know it would not be possible. By means of their remarkable green coloring matter, the *chlorophyll*, plants trap sun energy. They use this energy to split molecules of water into two parts, atoms of hydrogen and oxygen. Then they use the split-off hydrogen atoms to combine with carbon dioxide of the air to manufacture food. This food can be used by the plant or by an animal which eats the plant.

In spite of the many scientists who have studied photosynthesis since Ingenhousz, no one has ever quite solved the secret of how plants absorb the sun energy and put it to work.

Scientists have, however, learned a great deal about the process. They know that there are a number of steps — perhaps as many as thirty — between the water, carbon dioxide and sun energy taken in by the plant, and the food and oxygen produced.

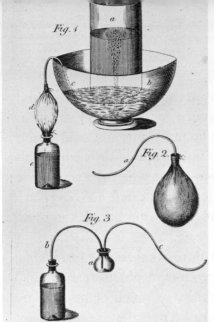

Left, illustration from Joseph Priestley's book, *Experiments and Observations on Different Kinds of Air*, showing how to collect what he called "fixed air," which we know as carbon dioxide. He put chalk and water into bottle e and added a small amount of "oil of vitriol" (sulphuric acid). The acid reacted with the carbonate and gave off carbon dioxide. When he shook bottle a, some of the gas dissolved in the water to make carbonated water. Right, closed system built by scientists at the University of California as a model for space studies. Algae plants grow in the tank at the bottom, and the mice live on the wires above it. The mice breathe oxygen given off by the algae and the algae use carbon dioxide breathed out by the mice.

Most of these steps, or chemical reactions, have been identified in recent years by means of radioactive tracer materials. In a laboratory at the University of California in Berkeley there are tall tubes, like thick fluorescent lamp tubes. These tubes stand upright and are filled with a bright green liquid. This liquid is water containing millions of tiny one-celled plants called green algae. The algae are growing in the light from lamps that are near the tubes.

The tiny plants are given doses of radioactive chemicals, especially radioactive carbon dioxide, by putting the chemicals into the water. Some of the atoms of these chemicals are breaking up so that they give off particles and waves that can be measured. They are something like the chemicals that are put in the radium dials of watches and clocks.

After the algae plants have taken the radioactive chemicals inside their walls, the plants are removed from the liquid and dried. They

Tiny algae plants are grown in ponds fertilized with sewage. Every so often the algae crop is harvested by being removed from the water with a centrifuge. The harvested crop, which looks like pulverized grass, is dried and mixed with stock feed. The mixture is being fed experimentally to sheep.

are then mashed up and tested. In the tests the radioactive chemicals can be identified because they leave traces on photographic paper. This clever and complicated method has the tongue-twisting name of paper chromatography.

By means of these experiments science has almost — but not quite — solved the last secret of photosynthesis.

We do know, however, that by this process plants have been the dependable guardians of man's existence since he first arrived on earth. At the same time they have manufactured food out of raw materials which neither man nor animals could eat, and made it possible for him and the animals to have nourishment. Man learned to eat both animal and plant foods.

Almost without exception man's plant foods have come from a certain kind of plants, the *seed plants*. The story of their beginning goes back to the time of the dinosaurs.

CHAPTER 3

PLANTS, DINOSAURS AND TRAVELING SEEDS

The Age of Reptiles, when the dinosaurs were on earth, lasted more than a hundred million years. Toward its end two things happened. One of them is one of the greatest riddles in the world of science. The other was the beginning of man's greatest source of food.

The world of dinosaurs was a warm world. It was a world of lush greenery and shallow seas. Even the regions of the North and South Poles had temperate climates. Water covered much of what is now Europe, Asia and the United States. Big plant-eating dinosaurs liked to wade near the shores of these seas where there were plenty of plants to eat and where the water partly supported the heavy weight of their huge bodies.

Most of the plants in this Age of Reptiles were different from today's plants. Many of them were big, like the dinosaurs that walked among them. The horsetail rushes, which you can crush with your feet as you wade through marshy places and along railroad tracks, were tall trees in that distant time. Crowding against these as the land became less boggy, were the forests of tree ferns with their long graceful fronds, forming gigantic tropical gardens.

Farther back from shore were many kinds of monkey-puzzle trees, whose modern descendants look as if they were badly made out of wire and plastic. Toward the middle of this long stretch of dinosaur time there were many kinds of cycads, waving their stiff palmlike branches. In the cooler parts of the world — although no part was as cold as the polar regions today — were some of the plants of today's temperate regions, such as the pines and the early hardwoods.

None of these plants had flowers. The plant world of the dinosaurs was a monotonous green. The beauty of flower color, that was to come into the world in later times, was still missing.

At the end of the great stretch of dinosaur time something happened which one scientist has called the "time of the great dying." The dinosaurs, who had been kings of the earth for such a long time, all perished. Never in the history of the world has there been such a great change in the living creatures. Not in one year did this happen. It took hundreds of thousands, perhaps even millions of years. But at the end of this period, not one dinosaur remained of all the many kinds that had roamed the land. Though there are many theories, scientists have never agreed on the answer to the riddle of why they all died.

As the Age of Reptiles passed, the climate became cooler and dryer. The seas shrank and new mountains were born. Great ice caps formed around the earth's poles. It was too cold in Alaska and Greenland for the oaks, the sassafras and other leafy trees. As the weather cooled, the warm-weather plants either died out or gradually migrated southward. Thus, for many plants, the end of the Age of Reptiles was also a time of dying. For the seed plants, it was a time of early and vigorous youth.

There had been seed plants before. The giant cycads that flourished in the Age of Reptiles had a primitive type of seed. These cycads have a few small relatives that we can see today. The coontie, a palmlike plant from Florida, is a cycad. So is the "potted palm" with stiff leaves often used by florists.

The giant ferns and horsetails had spores as today's ferns have. The fine brown dust that you can see when you shake dried ferns is made up of spores which will produce new ferns if conditions of warmth and moisture are favorable. There were also a few kinds of ferns that had primitive seeds.

The early seed plants depended on the wind to fertilize and scatter their seeds. The new kind of plants had both flowers and seeds. The flowers attracted insects to carry their pollen. The seeds were better than seeds had ever been before. They had seed coats that protected them against cold and water. It was lucky for man and his food supply that the seed plants developed these new ways.

Plants and animals change their ways very slowly. Those that change to something that makes them better fitted to their way of life have the advantage over their rivals. The seed plants had many advantages over their rivals, the plants with spores.

In 1939, a forest fire, now known as the Tillamook Burn, demonstrated one of the things that the seed plants could do better than the older kinds of plants.

The sun came up red in a cloudless sky that August morning in the Cascade mountains of Oregon. It was going to be another hot day. There was just a whisper of wind, the east wind — the dreaded fire wind. Everyone in the forest was uneasy. The men and women in the lookout stations kept scanning the sky and then looking at their humidity gauges. Humidity was low, too low for early morning. The lookouts knew a hot day could suck the last bit of moisture from the dead leaves and needles on the forest floor and the slashings left by lumbering.

The lumbermen were uneasy, too. "It's too dry," one of them said. "We'd better not cut today. One spark and all hell will pop."

As the day wore on the temperature kept going higher. It was nearly 100 degrees. The wind freshened. It was a hot, dry wind that sighed and whispered through the beautiful Douglas fir trees standing straight and tall and green on the sides of the mountains.

By one o'clock all logging had stopped except at one place on Gales Creek.

The boss logger wiped the sweat from his face. "It's too hot and dry to work any more," he said. "We'll bring in that one big log and then we'll call it a day." He gave the signal to start the machinery.

18

Then it happened. No one knew just how, but as the log was dragged to the landing, the friction on a stump or a cedar windfall must have caused a spark.

The loggers had fire-fighting tools — but they were down at the landing a few hundred feet away. Before the men could get them the fire had raced to the top of a tall snag. It burst into flame like a huge candle. The wind took hold of the burning bark and blew it a half mile across the canyon into the paper-dry slashings. The whole side of the mountain blew into fire like an explosion. A wall of flame rolled across the logged lands and hit the Douglas fir forest. It roared on through the two-hundred-foot firs like a hundred freight trains.

Men were called from the woods, from farms and from cities. A thousand men came to fight — two thousand men. It was all the same to the fire. It raced on and on. More than a week later, when it seemed about to be controlled, it exploded again into a hundred times its former violence. Huge thunderheads of smoke surged to a height of forty thousand feet. The very mountains seemed to be on fire. Many Pacific Coast cities were covered with ashes and burned needles. The sun was blotted out by a weird half-darkness. Ashes fell on ships five hundred miles at sea.

Nature finally came to the rescue of the desperate fire fighters. The terrible east wind changed and a moist cool fog drifted in from the Pacific. With its help the fire was finally stopped.

During those terrible eleven days a quarter of a million acres had been burned. The landscape looked dead for miles and miles. What could plants do after such a fire?

Three years later foresters went into the area to see if anything was growing. What plants had managed to send their seeds into this desolate place? What seeds could grow in such a garden?

There was much to remind the foresters of the terrible fire. Dead, black trees stood everywhere, a forest of burned-out chimneys. Some had been blown over by the wind and lay in piles. But the forest floor wasn't black any more. Color had come again to the land.

First there was fireweed. True to its name it had sent its seeds riding on their fluff parachutes to claim some of this empty land. There was the weed, groundsel, with its yellow flowers, which belong to the sunflower family. Botanists call it *senecia*, from the Latin word meaning *old man*, because its seed head topped with white fluff reminds them of white hair. Trailing among and around the other plants was a wild pea vine, which hadn't been common in the forest before the fire. Since its seeds are too heavy to be carried by the wind, this vine puzzled the experts.

"Just how this plant spread so widely and rapidly over such a large area, could not be answered," wrote one of the foresters.

There were other plants, too, such as Oregon grape with its leaves like English holly. There were blackberries, thimbleberries, ferns and bracken.

Best of all, there were baby trees — firs, cedars, spruces and maples. Even the terrible fire had not burned all the parent trees. A few had been spared in the moist low places. They had sent their seeds flying on the fall and winter winds. The forest was on its way again. Life was replacing death by means of the moving, scattering seeds.

Unfortunately, for the plants and for Oregon, the snags and dead trees were an invitation to another fire and still another. Twice in the next twelve years fire again swept the Tillamook area. Much of the land was burned so badly that even the seeds could not grow. All parent trees were gone. Shelter for baby plants was gone, too. Floods sloshed over the hills. Erosion set in. If the forest was to come back again man had to help.

This help the state of Oregon is giving now, with men and machines. The dead trees and dead wood on the ground are being removed. Men are setting out baby trees as fast as they can. Others are scattering Douglas fir seeds by airplanes, a half pound to the acre. Fire roads are being built. Fire lookouts and fire fighters are on the job. The baby trees are growing again. In a few years they will be scattering their seeds.

This ability to send their seeds traveling was one of the useful things that seed plants could do better than those plants which perished at the time of the great dying. To do this plants generally use the wind.

The seed plants are not the only ones that take advantage of the wind. Spores of ferns, mosses and other non-seed plants often journey great distances from the parent plant. Spores have been caught by airplanes at an altitude of more than two miles in the air. But the many clever devices for using the wind have distinguished the seed plants from other more ancient riders.

Many seeds have fine hairs that fluff out when the seeds are dry. Or they have fluff at the end of a tiny stem like a small umbrella. The majority of seeds of the most common flower family in the world, the sunflower family, are scattered this way. Many of our weeds like the daisy, thistle and dandelion belong to this family.

Dead timber, six years after Tillamook Burn. Note dense cover of fireweed.

The dandelion has another interesting way of helping its seeds get a good start into the air. When the flower blooms, the stem is still short, but as the seeds ripen the stem begins to grow again. When the seeds with their white parachutes are ready to fly away, the ball of fluff is high above the grass where the wind can catch it.

Many tree seeds ride the wind as they did in the Tillamook Burn. The seeds of willow, poplar and catalpa trees have tiny fluff parachutes. The sycamore packs several hundred seeds and their unopened 'chutes into a neat round ball. The seeds wait in the ball for their turn to fly, just as airmen with parachutes on their backs sit in an airplane. As the wind blows each seed out of the ball the parachute opens, and away it goes.

Other tree seeds, like the ash, the elm and the box elder, have wings that grow at the end or on each side. Pine tree seeds have thin wings that are hidden inside the cones until the seeds are ripe and the cones spread open. Many other tree seeds, including those of the giant sequoia, are provided with small winglike edges. A handful of seeds of the Hawaiian ironwood thrown into the air is said to resemble a swarm of fluttering insects.

These glider wings grow only on seeds of trees, tall bushes and high-climbing vines. They are never on seeds of small plants. One of the tropical vines of Indonesia, the anonia, which climbs into tall trees, has seeds with six-inch wings, thin as paper, that enable them to glide a half mile.

The tumbleweeds have a different scheme for using the wind. These plants grow into big round ball-like masses. When the seeds are dry and ready to be scattered the stem breaks off near the ground and the big ball rolls along before the winds, shaking out seeds as it goes.

The Russian thistle is a tumbleweed that Western farmers hate. It has rolled right across the western United States invading wheat fields and ranges. Sometimes its big balls pile up so high against fences that the fences are broken.

Native to the plains of Russia and Western Siberia, this thistle was first brought to the United States in some Russian flax seed. The flax (and thistle) seeds were sown in South Dakota in 1874. By 1895 the

Russian tumbleweed had rolled into sixteen states and thirteen Canadian provinces and had reached California. Since one plant can produce as many as a hundred thousand seeds it is not an easy plant to stop once it gets started.

Plants also have developed ways to use the animals and birds to help them scatter their seeds. The burdock has hooks curved like fishhooks on the outside of the seed head. When the hooks are green they are soft and no danger to anyone. It is not until the seeds are ripe and ready to be scattered that the hooks become hard and ready to grab onto the fur of any passing animal. Ten percent of all seed plants have some kind of spines or stickers to help scatter their seeds. You can picture many of these seeds from the names that have been given to them. Such names as beggar-ticks, stick-tights, pitchforks, sand burrs, puncture weed and devil's horns, show what people think of them.

Cowboys of the Western states hate the plants whose pretty yellow flowers are followed by pods with two wicked claws, the devil's horns. These claws catch the legs of horses or cows until the animals are crazy with pain. And even lions have been killed by the grapple plant of Africa. Once its three-inch claws fasten into the lion's mouth, the poor beast starves to death.

Other plants have a much more pleasant way to enlist the help of animals. These are the plants with fruits and berries. The covering around these seeds is sour and unpleasant until the seeds are ripe. Then the sweet juicy pulp offers a free meal to any bird or animal that comes along. Many seeds are spoiled in the animal's digestive tract, but many pass through unharmed. Others are carried off by birds to eat at a distance, and are dropped and scattered far away from the parent plant.

Many seeds are scattered over long distances by the moving currents of rivers and oceans. Only seeds with coats or pods that help them float can travel this way.

A scientist interested in seeds was the first person to write a scientific paper about the mighty Gulf Stream. Hans Sloane, a botanist, read about some seeds that another man, James Wallace, had found in the Orkney Islands, off the coast of Scotland. Wallace said he had found the "pretty nutts cast up on the shoar."

Sloane knew that these seeds grew only on the Island of Jamaica. He was amazed at the distance they had traveled. Sloane's paper about the seeds and the ocean currents was published in England in 1696. It was not until seventy years later that the first chart of the Gulf Stream was made. It was drawn under the direction of Benjamin Franklin by an American sea captain, Timothy Folger.

The coconut is another seed that will float long distances in the water. The hard inner shell of the coconut is watertight, and this is wrapped in an outer husk. Many air spaces in this husk make it a fine floater. Coconuts have been found in the ocean thousands of miles from their native shores.

Perhaps an even better floater is the gourd. It's so light that native fishermen have often used gourds for floats on their fishing nets. Cultivated in both Africa and America for its hard woody shell, the gourd does not grow wild on either continent. It's only found where there are people, who use it for containers and dippers and to make musical instruments, as well as floats. It has been so long with man that its wild ancestors have been lost. Gourds have been found in South America with relics of ancient people who lived long before modern man began moving around the world.

Two scientists, Dr. Thomas Whitaker and Dr. George Carter, did an experiment to see how long gourds could float in sea water and still contain seeds that would sprout. For the experiment they arranged to keep sea water flowing through two bathtubs. Then they put twelve gourds into each tub. Once a month they took out a gourd, broke it open and planted a hundred of its seeds.

They found that gourds could float in sea water for 347 days, and still have seeds that would grow. They reported that the baby plants were healthy and vigorous. When they investigated the speed of drift of the ocean currents from Africa to Brazil they learned that a floating object could make the trip in as little as five months. This showed that gourds could have originated first in Africa and then drifted to South America, as many scientists have believed.

During the millions of years since the Age of Reptiles the number of clever devices developed by seed plants is almost beyond the telling. The wild oats in the California hills have awns or tails that curl and uncurl as the air becomes dryer or wetter. Such seeds use this curling method to screw themselves into the ground or into the wool or hides of animals.

Plants such as the common violet, thyme and sage pack their seeds into pods that crack open and shoot out the seeds when anything touches them. One gardener complained because he found it so hard to collect any seeds of the salvia growing in his garden.

"The plant shot them all away before I could get to them," he said.

All these devices have gradually formed in the various seed plants and have been retained. They help the plants scatter their seeds so they won't perish as the dinosaurs did.

Remember, these are wild seeds we are talking about. When man arrived on the scene he had mixed feelings about the scattering seeds. Some ten thousand years ago he began to do something about it. But before he did this, he had good reasons to know how easily seeds fall off the parent plant once they are ripe. The hunter-gatherer peoples had to know just when to pick the seeds so they would be ripe enough to eat, yet not so ripe that they had all been scattered from the parent plants. Those peoples needed other skills too in order to survive, as we shall see in the next chapter.

CHAPTER 4

THE CAVE MEN

This is the story of the food hunters and gatherers, people who ate only what they could find in the woods, fields and streams. It is also the story of two caves and the scientific detective work that unraveled their story.

Naturally, after thousands of years it is hard to tell just what ancient people did, people such as the hunters and gatherers. They had not yet learned to write so there is no written record. City people leave stone or mud walls or houses that can be excavated and studied. But the hunters and gatherers didn't live in cities. They couldn't. There wasn't enough food in one place for a large group of people. Scientists have to figure out their story from the few things they left behind. These are called *artifacts*. Stone objects such as weapons and knives or paintings on cliffs and cave walls last longest. However, sometimes other things made of wood or even straw last surprisingly well in dry climates.

One of the best places to piece together the jigsaw puzzle of the ancient story of man is in certain caves. Here, the scientist-explorer may slice down through the accumulated trash of ten or twenty thousand years. Often there are definite layers in the dirt, like the layers of a cake. Sometimes these layers are divided by thin stone deposits as cake layers are separated by icing. The scientist can read the stories of the ancient men in each layer.

A cave near Wendover, Utah, has had several names. Local people called it Hands and Knees Cave, because the entrance was so small they had to crawl to get inside. Later, it became known as Danger Cave because many big rocks fell from the cliff, almost crushing some cave explorers.

Danger Cave is in the side of a rocky hill which overlooks the gleaming white salt flats on the Great Salt Desert in Utah. The country around it is cold in winter and unbearably hot and dry in summer. Nothing grows on the white flats, and only desert plants such as saltbush and pickleweeds grow on the nearby hills.

When Dr. Jesse David Jennings, a scientist, and his crew first started to work there, Danger Cave seemed quite shallow, with a rocky overhang like a porch roof. At the back they found a low narrow tunnel. When they crawled through this they entered a room as big as a gymnasium with a domed roof.

"It was huge, cool and completely dark," Dr. Jennings said.

He and his crew of scientists, laborers and students brought shovels and pickaxes and started to work. They dug a trench through the outer room and into the big cavern. It was hard work. There were big boulders in the way that had to be lifted. Much of the dirt was very fine, and as they worked the cave filled with dust like thick smoke. All the workmen had to wear dust masks. Every bit of dirt had to be carried outside. Then it had to be put through a coarse wire screen so that nothing which the ancient cave men had left would be lost.

The trench grew longer and deeper — eight, ten, twelve feet deep. Every five feet the scientists would stop digging, brush off the vertical sides of the big ditch and examine it carefully. There before their eyes was history written in dirt. A brown layer an inch thick might be all that was left of a thousand years of living of the cave people. Sometimes there would be pieces of flint or bone sticking in the sides of the trench like raisins in a muffin. Digging this trench was like a continuous treasure hunt.

The oldest layers, of course, were at the bottom of the trench, nearest the stone floor of the cave. The scientists examined the first, or oldest layer, the one lying on the stone of the cave floor. It wasn't made of that fine dust that had been filling their noses and choking their breathing. Instead, it was made entirely of small stones like gravel. They were cemented together with a natural lime cement. The little stones were rounded and worn-looking as if they had been a long time in a stream or lake.

"There's no question about it," Dr. Jennings said. "The gravel was washed into the cave by lake water."

He knew that the lake must have dried up thousands of years ago. All that was left were the layers of salt on the flats and a few marshy places that formed when it rained. But once long ago the lake had washed in and out of the cave. At this ancient time the lake was about ninety feet deep.

On top of the worn gravel was a layer of clean, gray sand, with tiny fossil shells mixed in it.

"This, too, must have been brought into the cave by the lake water," Dr. Jennings said. "The waves were more gentle at this time. Probably the lake was already shrinking."

At six places in the gray sand the scientists found something even more exciting. They were not much to look at, only small pockets of charcoal, about three feet in diameter. But charcoal deep inside a cave! And in a circle with ten feet of accumulated trash on top! It could only mean that shortly after the lake had shrunk enough to leave the cave dry, ancient men had come into the cave for shelter, and had built a fire. Not once, but six times had they come and built a campfire.

What had these men — and perhaps women and children — thought of as they sat around these ancient fires? The lake, now shrunken and dry, must have been blue and sparkling in front of the cave. Perhaps a cold wind blew off it, so that was the reason for the fire. Or, maybe the fires were for another purpose. A few jasper chips were found nearby, and a beautifully chipped point for a dart or spear. Maybe the men had speared some fish and the women were cooking them.

30

How long ago had this been? How long does it take a lake ninety feet deep to dry up completely? How many thousand years is required to accumulate enough trash from living to pile fourteen feet high in a cave? This trash had collected century upon century from people and animals until, ten feet back from the cave entrance, it touched the roof.

Until 1955 these would have been hard questions to answer. However, in this year two professors at the University of Chicago, Drs. Arnold and Libby, worked out a method for finding the age of certain kinds of ancient objects. They did it by using radioactivity.

These professors pointed out that all living things, both plants and animals, have a substance in them known as carbon. Of course, many other things contain carbon, too. Pencil lead is almost pure carbon, and so are diamonds. However, living things, especially, contain carbon.

The carbon of charcoal came into the wood as the gas, carbon dioxide, when the tree was alive. Some of this carbon is a special kind known as carbon-14. This peculiar carbon was formed in a very special way by the action of cosmic rays on part of our air.

All living things have in them some of this special carbon that they got from the air. You and I have, and so have all other animals and plants. As soon as anything dies it does not receive any more of this special carbon-14. And what it has begins to break up and change back into the ordinary form of carbon.

The professors found that all dead things do this breaking up or changing back at the same rate, so the more carbon-14 that has gone back to ordinary carbon, the older is the object.

There is one thing troublesome about this method. The thing to be studied or dated has to be first changed to carbon. In other words it has to be burned. Sometimes scientists do not want to burn their valuable specimens just to find how old they are. Other things such as flint and arrowheads don't have any carbon in them.

In the case of the campfire remains in Danger Cave, the wood was already burned to charcoal, or carbon. Dr. Jennings sent it to the Chicago laboratory to find out how old it was. When the answer came back, he and his helpers were astounded. The ancient campfires in the cave had been extinguished eleven thousand years ago. Imagine, *eleven thousand years*. This was the oldest proof ever found for man in the New World.

The layers above the gray sand told their story, too. When the dirt had been removed from the trenches and sifted, there were more than three thousand stone knives, spear points and arrowheads to be examined and studied.

There were thousands of other objects, too, or pieces of objects, that the cave people had used. Mostly these showed hard usage. Few of the things were whole or in good condition. They had obviously been thrown away only because they were worn out. This showed that the people who had used Danger Cave were not careless or thriftless.

The baskets were in shreds, or at least had big holes in them. Moccasins were worn until they must have almost fallen from the feet of the wearer. One pair had big patches on the heel and toe. One patch had been worn until it, too, had a hole and then another patch had been sewn on top of the first.

Many of the arrowheads and spear points were broken. The stone knives were dull from use. Only short pieces of string were found except in a few cases. The good long strings had evidently been taken away when the people left the cave. String is precious when it has to be made by hand from fiber stripped out of plant stems.

Everything had to be properly recorded. Every layer of dirt had to be noted separately and the things which came from it listed. A number of pieces of wood or leather or string from each dirt layer were sent to be burned and carbon-14 tested, so the age of each layer would be known.

As the scientists expected, the things found higher up in the trench were not as old as the charcoal from the campfires on the lake gravel. The youngest thing found in the dirt was dated a few years after Christ.

When everything had been studied, Dr. Jennings was ready to describe the people who had used Danger Cave for nearly a *hundred centuries*. Surprisingly enough, the more ancient peoples had not been too different from the later ones. And they were all quite similar in their way of life to the Indians who were living in that area when the white men came.

The ancients were hunters and gatherers. They ate what they could find from day to day. The tiny seeds of the pickleweed bush had served them many a meal. Tons of the dried bushes, threshed clean of all seeds, were found trampled into the dirt of the cave. Many grinding stones, most of them well worn or broken, were also found. These had been used to crack the tough seed coats. Perhaps the seeds had then been cooked into a mush. Other kinds of seeds were found, too, as well as remnants of plant roots which had been eaten.

They were clever people, these cave men and women of ancient Utah. They knew how to chip flint and volcanic glass into a fine knife or a point for a weapon. The women were expert basket-makers. They made at least fourteen different kinds of baskets. They also knew how to weave mats and simple cloth. They could make fine strong string that compares with the best made by our factories today. Their string was made with fingers and teeth, and probably given the proper twist by being rolled against a naked thigh, as some native peoples do today.

The cave people had leather which they had tanned, and needles and thread. The thread was made of sinew from the tendons of animals, or of small strips of buckskin. These show that the cave people must have worn clothes, although only scraps were found.

Danger Cave was not a year-round home, Dr. Jennings decided from his studies. Everything pointed to the conclusion that the people had come and stayed a while and then left. Perhaps they came in the fall for the pickleweed crop. While the women and children collected the tiny seeds and mashed them on grinding stones the men were out hunting. At night they gathered in the cave. There they had food, and a fire for cooking and warmth. The cave must have seemed quite cozy. They slept on piles of threshed pickleweed bushes or on tule leaves which are like those of cattails. The later people may have had a rabbitskin blanket or two. Part of one of these woven blankets was found in the cave dirt.

Many cave people lived in the cave only when it suited their needs at the time, scientists think. They were busy people, because their search for food was continuous. When it was gone in one place they moved on to another. They were the first migrants, going from one wild crop to another.

In the winter they ate nuts and seeds they had collected and stored. They ate the meat of animals or fish which the men caught. While they lived in Danger Cave, however, they ate mostly seeds and roots. In other words, they were getting their food from the stored food of the seed plants — food stored in root, stem and seed.

Many other caves have been excavated, both in America and in Europe and Africa. Twenty years before the work at Danger, another cave had been studied by scientists. This one, also, is in the Great Basin of the western United States, the site of so many huge lakes during the last ice age. Sixteen miles from Las Vegas, Nevada, Gypsum Cave is named for the crystals that decorate many of its walls. It is a big cave with a big entrance, big enough to drag a house through except for the fallen rocks that bar it. The cave is well known to many people who live in that part of the country. Many of them have gone exploring in its black depths. Others have enjoyed picnics in its sunny mouth.

The old-timers in those parts tell many stories about the cave. One relates how a band of fierce Apache Indians were chased out of Arizona and hid in the cave, together with their horses. That was the reason, the old-timers said, that the floor of the cave looked like an abandoned stable.

Dr. Mark Harrington, the scientist who studied the cave, thought the floor did look like an ancient stable. Only he thought it didn't look quite as it should if horses had been stabled there. He had a hunch that other animals had used the cave, much bigger animals than horses.

His hunch proved right. Even before the digging had gone very far, his secretary, poking around in the black crevices with her flashlight, found something. It was an object that looked different from the rocks around it. She pulled it out and carried it to her employer.

"Look what I found," she said. "It looks like the skull of some animal, but it's so big."

34

Fossil claws of giant ground sloth

Dr. Harrington's hands must have been a little unsteady as he reached for her treasure. "I think I know what it is," he told her. "But let's send it to the experts and be sure."

Before the report came back, another lady, a visitor, went cave exploring. She found not one bone but a whole pile of them partly buried by a column of white stone. This column was a stalagmite, a deposit of calcium carbonate, resembling an inverted icicle, that had been formed on the cave floor thousands of years before by dripping water. When she reported her find, the scientists discovered other bones nearby. Even better than these, they found a huge claw with some skin and yellow-brown hair still fastened to it. Then Dr. Harrington was sure.

"No living creature has such a claw today," he said when he saw it. "It must have belonged to a giant ground sloth."

No modern man ever saw this ground sloth. Neither does anyone know exactly how long ago the last one perished. Were there men present at that time? Or was this before man came to North America? This is the question the scientists asked the trench in the cave floor to answer.

The answer was there. Gravel and rocks were found washed into this cave, too, in ancient rainy times. On top of the gravel, campfire circles were found, and on top of them were sloth droppings. Above this was a layer of unbroken rock formed by water dripping in wet centuries. At another place the scientists found the bones of a baby sloth, and nearby the chipped flint point made by some ancient man. There was no question that man had been there when the sloths were still alive.

The trench in the cave told other things about the people who had used it. They, too, had been hunters and gatherers, and had lived on roots, seeds and nuts. The seeds of many plants were found — of the mesquite, the screwbean, the catclaw. There were grinding stones and flat stones to rub them on. The stone knives were there, the dart points and the arrowheads. But something else was there in abundance.

Grinding stones (metate and mano) found in Gypsum Cave

This something else was bones. These were the bones of the animals which the cave people had eaten. There were bones of mountain sheep, of an extinct camel, and others. Many looked as if the people had chewed off the meat and then cracked the bones to get at the sweet nutritious marrow inside.

36

Artist's reproduction of extinct giant ground sloth

And there were cracked sloth bones, too, some with scratches made by flint knives. Apparently the ancients had somehow managed to kill the giant sloths so they could use them for food. Were there mighty battles in Gypsum Cave when man pitted his puny strength against the huge animals? This the dirt history didn't answer. Neither did it answer how long ago the sloth feast had taken place, since the radiocarbon dating method had not been discovered when the excavations at Gypsum were carried out.

Since that time a few specimens from Gypsum have been radiocarbon tested. From these tests it seems that men were not in Gypsum any sooner than they were in Danger. Why then, didn't the cave people at Danger eat sloth meat, too?

There is no sure answer to this question except to assume that there weren't any sloths around Danger Cave. And there were no camels or horses either. There were bones found in Danger, but they were those of smaller animals. Neither were there as many bones as were found in Gypsum.

The cave dirt seems to say that the hunter and gatherer peoples ate what they could find. If there was meat they ate it. If meat was scarce they ate more seeds and roots and berries.

In New Mexico ancient stone points have been found stuck between the ribs of giant extinct bison. And in South Dakota stone points were found lying among the bones of the mammoth. This was a kill that would have fed many for as long as the meat would keep without spoiling.

How long ago were these ancients in America? Scientists don't know. The eleven-thousand-year date at Danger Cave is the oldest authentic date so far. Most scientists agree that the ancients came from Asia during the last ice age when much of the water from the oceans was frozen into glaciers. At that time the oceans were so lowered that there must have been a land bridge where Bering Strait is today. Perhaps the hunter-gatherer people followed the game animals across the bridge. No one, even scientists who have studied the evidence for years, knows for sure.

They do know that woven sandals were found in a cave in Oregon that radiocarbon dated at ten thousand years. Then there are the campfires at Danger Cave, proof that man has been in America a long time. And the cave artifacts prove, too, that cave men had already gone a long way in the steps toward a system of food gathering and toward civilization.

CHAPTER 5

BASKETS, DIGGING STICKS AND ISHI

Many of the hunter-gatherer people, such as the early cave men, became very clever at collecting food. They knew just where each kind of plant grew in their territory and when it would be ready for use. They knew the uses of each plant: whether it was good for food, for medicine or for fiber.

They were good hunters. They made stone or bone weapons to kill the animals in the forests and plains. Scientists have studied these weapons and found they were sharp and deadly. A scientist at the University of California tested obsidian (volcanic glass) arrowheads and found that arrows tipped with obsidian penetrated flesh better than those with modern steel tips.

The women who gathered seeds first had to make the containers they were to use. Indian women, in what is now called California, made baskets of all kinds, shapes and sizes. Some were coarse for separating the seeds from leaves and chaff. Others were sewed so tightly they would hold water. Some of these baskets, made with only primitive tools, have thirty stitches to the inch. Indian women still make these baskets today. One such basket, seven and a half inches high, had fifty thousand stitches and required seven months to complete.

With such skill it's no wonder that some of the hunter-gatherer people lived this life until comparatively recent times. Even today they linger on in a few remote parts of the world, such as Australia and Central Africa.

The last stone-age man found in the United States was discovered near Oroville, California, in August 1911. He was given the name of Ishi.

Oroville is a small town in the north central part of the state, on the eastern edge of the great central valley. Dull green olive orchards and groves of golden oranges spread out from the edge of town toward the foothills of the Sierra mountains.

In the 1800's Oroville was a bustling gold-mining town, but by 1911 it was much the same pleasant village it is today. Boys played baseball and rode bicycles in the streets. Women did their house-work and went shopping. Nobody there was expecting to meet a wild Indian, especially the butcher's boy.

It was early in the morning and the boy was probably sleepy. His attention was attracted to the corral back of the slaughterhouse by the hysterical barking of a dog. When he went to see what the dog was so excited about, he saw Ishi squatting against the back fence.

The boy ran to tell his employers. Almost immediately everybody was excited. In those days people knew what to do about a runaway horse or an escaped steer. But a wild Indian!

Ishi — who was, of course, nameless at this time — didn't look very dangerous sitting there against the back fence, nearly dead from starvation and exhaustion. However, the people of Oroville knew he *must* be dangerous. Wasn't he an almost naked Indian, and wild?

So the police were sent for. They arrived hastily and gave Ishi an old butcher's apron, put handcuffs on him, and took him off to the town jail.

Ishi went with them willingly enough. They put him behind the bars and gave him some food to eat and water to drink but he wouldn't touch a thing. He wouldn't talk either. At least he wouldn't talk in any language anybody could understand.

His jailers spoke to him in English and Spanish, but Ishi only shook his head that he didn't understand. They sent for several kinds of Indians who tried out their languages, but none seemed to make any impression.

The town became more and more excited and curious. The papers ran feature stories under big headlines. People crowded into the jail to get a look at the wild Indian. They had to be forcibly put out by the sheriff.

Finally the headlines reached San Francisco papers, where scientists at the University's anthropology museum read them. They were even more excited than the Oroville people, but for a very different reason.

If Ishi couldn't talk the ordinary Indian language of the valley Indians he must be from the hills to the east of Oroville. The scientists knew the history of these hill dwellers. They recalled how these Indians had fought the white men crowding into their homeland. They had hung on desperately against overwhelming opposition, until all but a few had perished. There was scarcely any record of their way of life in California where they had been for at least two thousand years.

The scientists were particularly interested in one tribe. This tribe was the Yahi, the southernmost division of the Yana peoples. Scarcely ever numbering more than 2,000 members, the Yahis had vanished from the foothills. Even their language was lost. Scientists had dreamed of finding someone from this lost tribe — a voice from the past — but there seemed little likelihood that it would happen.

Could this wild Indian in the Oroville jail possibly be a living remnant of the lost tribe? Scientists hardly dared hope. However, just in case, they sent a telegram to the Oroville jail asking the sheriff to hold the Indian until they could get there.

One of the scientists, Dr. Waterman, hurried to the foothill town, taking with him a paper on which was written a list of words from the languages of two other tribes of the Yana peoples.

Sitting down on a cot in the jail cell next to the unhappy Indian, Dr. Waterman began to read word after word from the list. As the dark eyes of the Indian watched he pronounced the difficult syllables as best he could. There was not a flicker of interest or recognition

41

from the savage beside him. Only doubt and suspicion showed on his face.

It was discouraging work, Dr. Waterman related afterward. He was more than half way down the list when he said the word "siwini," which was supposed to mean "pine." As he said the word he patted the pine wood of the cot on which the two men were sitting.

All at once the face of the Indian changed. He smiled for the first time since he had been behind the bars. "Siwini," he said, correcting the scientist in his pronunciation, and patting the pine of the cot.

Then, according to Dr. Waterman's account, the scientist and the wild Indian sat there grinning at each other and patting the pine wood of the cot and saying the only word they both knew over and over. "Siwini, siwini." At last the language barrier had been broken.

From this beginning a few other words were found on the list that the Indian knew. Soon, the authorities located another Indian, Sam Batwi, in a nearby town. He belonged to a different division of the Yana, than Ishi. Sam and Ishi could understand each other with difficulty. Since Sam also spoke English, he could tell the scientists some of the things Ishi was saying. Dr. Waterman felt certain that Ishi was the last member of the Yahi, the long-lost tribe.

In a few days, Ishi was taken on the train to San Francisco and given a room in the Museum of Anthropology. Ishi started to learn English, while Dr. Waterman and his chief, Dr. Kroeber, began the study of Ishi's difficult language.

Ishi was also given his name, since according to the Indian tradition he refused to speak his own name. Dr. Kroeber told reporters that he was to be known as "Ishi," which was the word for "man" in Ishi's language. Ishi never spoke this name either, but he answered to it. Later, he learned to write it legibly enough to sign checks.

Ishi also had a great deal to learn about the white man's civilization. Although he had lived all his life within a hundred miles of Oroville, he had avoided all contact with white people because he considered them to be enemies of his people. He had come into town that August morning only as a last resort, driven by hunger and loneliness after all of his tribe but him were dead.

Left, Ishi shoots bow and arrow; middle, Ishi prepares to harpoon salmon; bottom, Ishi retrieves arrow.

Ishi had a good mind and was an apt pupil. He learned about automobiles and street cars. He learned about stores and money. He found out that white men told the time of day by clocks instead of by the sun and stars. He saw that most men worked and were given wages for their labor. Ishi, too, wanted a job. In the short space of three months, Ishi's wish came true. He was so well adapted to his new life that he was hired as an assistant janitor at the museum.

The scientists at the museum learned a great deal from Ishi, who had been the son of a chief and was well-educated in his own culture. This stone-age Indian gave them an account of the life of his tribe as it had been lived for two thousand years in one part of California. He showed them how he made fire without matches. He fashioned bows and arrows, and tipped them with arrowheads which he made out of obsidian. He was an excellent craftsman; everything he made showed fine workmanship. He told them how his people had found all their food in the woods and fields, and how they had cooked it.

Most of the tribes of California Indians, including Ishi's people, had three staple foods, acorns, fish and deer meat.

The acorns were gathered in the fall. If the oaks were too far from the homes of the tribe, the families went on a camping trip to the oak groves to harvest the nuts. They came home heavily laden. Every member of the tribe — man, woman or child — carried as many as he could. Acorns not eaten right away were stored unshelled, in small storage huts made for the purpose.

Before the acorns could be eaten there was a great deal of hard work to do. The nuts had to be shelled, ground to flour, and then leached or soaked in water. The leaching was necessary because of the bitter chemical, tannin, which most acorns contain. Nobody knows who first learned to leach the tannin out of acorns, or how many thousand years ago this was first done. Almost every California Indian woman knew how to do this, and how to make bread and mush from the prepared flour. This was part of her work, and she did it as a matter of course.

After she had cracked the acorns and picked them out from the broken shells, she put them into a mortar, which is a strong bowl-shaped container, and pounded them into a coarse powder. Some-

Leaching acorn flour in hole lined with sand. Hot rock will heat water in basket.

times the mortar was nicely made out of stone, and sometimes it was a hole in the granite rock, conveniently near the oak trees.

If you should go hiking along the oak-bordered streams in California you might find some of these mortar-holes in the granite ledges, as they are common in the California foothills. Sometimes there are several of them together, spaced at convenient distances. It is easy to picture the Indian women sitting there in the warm sun of a California autumn, cracking and grinding their winter's food supply, while they chatted and laughed as they worked. The holes, smooth and cone-shaped, are about eight or nine inches deep and five or six inches across. They are often known locally as Indian "pot

45

holes," but they were not used for cooking, but for grinding. An Indian woman had a hard smooth creek rock, shaped like a small loaf of French bread, which she pounded and turned inside the hole.

The leaching process took several hours. Some California Indians made a hole in the ground and lined it with sand or cedar bark, then filled the hole with acorn meal. Next, water was poured into the hole and allowed to drain out slowly. This had to be done several times before the acorn meal had lost its bitter taste and was considered edible. Usually the water was heated for the last three times.

Even the heating of the water, the way the Indians had to do it, would be considered quite a task by the modern housewife. Since the Indians had no metal cooking vessels, they heated water in tightly woven baskets by dropping in hot rocks. First, of course, they had to heat the rocks in a campfire, take them out with a rock-holder made of a specially bent stick, wash off the soot, and then drop them into the basket of water.

Other California Indian tribes did the whole process in baskets, from the leaching through the cooking. The mush was cooked in the same way the water was heated, by dropping hot rocks into the mixture of acorn meal and water.

"It was surprising how fast the mush could be cooked in this way," one old-timer said. "And it was good, too."

California Indian women often made acorn bread out of the leached meal. Most modern Indians have lost not only the ability to make this bread but also the taste for it. However, even today, there are a few Indian women who can make tasty bread out of acorns.

Some dietitians have claimed that if the California Indians had depended wholly upon their three staples, acorn meal, fish and deer meat, they would have been a poorly nourished lot, because much of the vitamin content was soaked out of the acorns by the water. Indian housewives, of course, knew nothing about vitamins, but like most primitive women, they served their families a varied diet of roots, bulbs, seeds and berries, as they became ripe and ready to eat in the woods and fields.

As soon as the early spring came to California the Indian house-

46

wives were out in the meadows searching for edible greens. A little later it was the roots and bulbs of some of the spring wildflowers, such as the camas, the tiger lily, the brodiaea and the Mariposa lily. An hour's digging with the pointed digging stick was said to give enough lily roots for a meal. In the summer, they picked blackberries, thimbleberries and fox grapes. Most of these were eaten fresh but some were dried for winter.

The women made special collecting baskets, designed for the kind of thing they were going to gather. You can see them in the museums today. There are coarsely woven ones for the roots, and very finely woven ones for the fine seeds. There are huge cone-shaped baskets for carrying acorns. Then there are the scoop-shaped *beaters*, used to brush the fine seeds from the bush to the baskets, because the wild seeds waited for nobody. They had to be brushed off at just the right time, or they would be scattered by the winds.

Scientists who have studied the food of the California Indians say there were several hundred plants that they used for food and medicine. Every woman was a specialist. She had to be. If she weren't she would have soon poisoned her family. For instance, there are two kinds of camas lilies in the California marshes. One has an edible root, the other is deadly poison. No Indian woman had any trouble telling them apart. She had learned about them from her mother when she was a little girl.

The California Indians' year was an orderly one. They did not live hit or miss. Each month brought its duties and pleasures. Much of each month's activities depended on the kinds of foods that could be obtained at that time.

Spring was the time for gathering and cooking the early greens and bulbs. Then there were small animals to be caught, as well as geese and fish. Perhaps the family might go on a camping trip to some nearby lake to enjoy the ducks and lake fish. Usually there were some piñon nuts, which are the seeds of certain low-growing pines, and acorns left over from winter supplies, to round out the menu.

In summer there were many small seeds ripe in the fields. Women and children went out to gather seeds, bulbs and berries, much as our pioneer women did.

One ancient Indian said, remembering the olden days, "People went out in large groups, leaving the houses early in the morning and returning in the evening."

July was the season for drying fruits and seeds, and the time to make Indian candy. Aside from honey, which had to be taken from angry bees, sweets were scarce in California Indian times. However, there was one kind of sweet that someone in the dim past had found how to make. It took a lot of hard work, but Indian women were used to that.

There was a certain kind of tall plant or cane on which the ants placed aphids, tiny insects which suck sweet juice from plants. After the aphids had been on the canes for a while there were sticky crystals of sugar on the leaves and stalks.

The Indians cut the canes, spread them in the hot sun, heaped them on bearskins and beat them hard with sticks. Then the crystals were scraped off the bearskins, shaken in a flat basket tray to get out the dry leaves and twigs, put in a small cooking basket with a little water and kneaded into a stiff dough. After a week, this had dried into a hard brown loaf, from which pieces could be broken off to be eaten with mush or given to the children as a treat.

One old Indian said, "The little bugs make the sugar on the cane, like bees, and then fly away. The bugs weren't on the cane when it was pounded."

The California Indians also made chewing gum from the juice of one kind of milkweed. It was collected into the hollow stalk of another plant and roasted in hot ashes until the juice thickened.

"It was better than store gum," an Indian woman said.

Fall was the time of year to gather the all-important acorns. Some kinds were prized above others because they had less of the bitter tannin and were sweeter. Tribes that had none of the sweet acorns often made trips into the territory of a neighboring tribe, if they were friendly.

"All the people except the very old persons and young children

48

went together to get acorns," an Indian recalled. "The women collected them while the men hunted and trapped."

Another important event in the Indian year was the trip to the mountains to gather piñon nuts. Since it was a long way to the mountains the people had to do some planning.

Everyone watched the berries on a certain bush (*Rhamnus californica*) that grew in the lowlands. When the berries on this bush turned red, the Indians knew the piñon nuts were ripe in the mountains. Just to be doubly sure a man was sent into the mountains to scout out the best trees.

"Some men went out first to see where the piñons were good," an old Indian recalled. "They decided. Then everybody went to the places where these men said the nuts were."

And so the year passed. Winter was a time for staying in the huts out of the cold rains and winds. There were plenty of acorns and other nuts, as well as dried berries and deer meat. There was a fire for warmth and stories to tell over and over. There was work for all: baskets for women to sew, weapons for the men to fashion.

Nowhere in California, except in the extreme southeastern part on the Colorado River, was there any agriculture. Over most of what is now the United States, Indians planted small patches of corn, beans and squash. But not in California.

Why was it that the Californians, almost alone among the American Indians, had not progressed from wild plants to tame ones for at least part of their food?

Many experts have tried to answer this question. Some have said that it was the lack of summer rains that made things harder to grow. Others say, no. The Spaniards grew crops when they arrived and the Indians could have also, if they had been interested.

Most experts agree that it was the bountiful supplies furnished by nature. This was the reason the Indians of this state remained in the hunter-gatherer stage more than a thousand years after other Indians of the continent had changed to planting and reaping.

Nowhere in California is there any Indian tale of hunger or starvation. No ancient sage tells of lean times when the people suffered from lack of food. California, in ancient times as at present, was a bountiful supplier of food for its people.

White immigrants, Spaniards and Americans, ended the hunter-gatherer life of the California Indians. Ranchers came in and fenced off the land. Pigs and cattle ate the plants and acorns. Oak trees were cut down. Deer and small game became scarce and hard to get. Two thousand years of life habits were wiped out in less than a hundred years.

California Indians were forced to change their way of life or perish. Many of them did perish. Others stayed on the edge of the white man's civilization and begged, or earned a meager living. A few were able to change. Others are still trying to learn to live in this new world that has been forced upon them.

In other more remote parts of the world hunter-gatherer peoples still exist. In central Australia there are a few tribes that range over a wide territory gathering the wild foods as they ripen and killing wild animals.

These aborigines do not have houses of any kind and only a few possessions. Whole tribes live out their lives in nakedness with no knowledge of the modern world and none of its gadgets.

They know every plant and animal in their area. They have adapted well to their surroundings; they are masters of their environment. No white man can compete with them in their own land or could live in such a place without outside help.

Men, women and children can walk for two days or even three, if necessary, without food, and with almost no water, through the burning sands of the desert. They eat everything that offers a bit of nourishment and isn't poisonous. Such things as lizards, grubs, roots, birds, and snakes are common fare.

Their only tool is the digging stick; their weapons are the wooden boomerang and the stone-tipped spear.

Yet even here the white rancher is pushing in on the edges of this desert country. He is taking the better lands and leaving the ever poorer and poorer to the natives. A few of these natives are working for the white man; others are moving into the towns where they

50

Left, Chilean woman plants potatoes with digging stick; above, Indian woman uses winnowing basket.

somehow manage to survive. Soon these hunter-gatherer people will be forced to change or perish.

In Central and East Africa the story is similar. The bushmen, once supreme masters of their semi-desert country, are being crowded into poorer and poorer lands. Now they live always on the edge of starvation in spite of their skills.

These are the ends of a way of life that lasted many thousands of years longer than has the agricultural cultivation of tame plants. The ever mounting pressure of more and more people in the world has made agriculture a necessity for every civilization. The ancient ways of the hunter-gatherer are now all but impossible.

CHAPTER 6

A MODERN STONE-AGE FOOD—
WILD RICE

There is one grain food that you can buy in the grocery stores of the U.S. and Canada today, that goes as far back in time as there were people on this continent.

If you throw a handful of these grains into a pot of boiling water along with a few pieces of wild game, say duck or rabbit, you will taste the same flavors as did the people who lived thousands of years ago. The only difference is that their dinner was cooked in a basket with hot rocks instead of in a pan on a gas or electric stove.

This food is wild rice. Although it isn't a true rice, the grains look something like stretched-out kernels of rice. It grows in water as true rice does.

Wherever wild rice grew the Indians considered themselves fortunate. This was a treasured food, a food given them by the gods. They fought many battles to keep other hunter-gatherer people from reaping it.

Today in the stores, wild rice is the highest priced cereal in the world. Even though it is boxed in a fancy box at a modern mill, it is still as wild and untamed as when it was first eaten by man. No scientist has changed it by experimentation. Nor has it been crossed with any other grass.

As you chew the nut-flavored kernels, picture to yourself the ancient peoples that lived in the beautiful northern lake country of the United States and Canada.

It is early fall. The manomini moon, the wild rice moon, shines white each night. Its light is almost as bright as day, turning the ripples on the lake to silver. From the distance comes the quavering call of a loon, and closer is the splash of fish jumping in the shallows. Thousands of ducks are quacking their last sleepy talk to each other before quieting for the night. A warm wind, the manomini wind, soft as velvet, brings a rich scent of night and green things in water.

This is the day the people come to the lake. They have come for the wild rice harvest. There are young men and women, old people and children. Many are related. They have brought their few household possessions and have set up camp along the shores. There is noise and confusion, with dogs running and barking, and getting in everyone's way. Aunts, uncles, cousins, greet each other and talk of everything that has happened since they were last together. The moon is so bright that nobody wants to go to bed. Everyone is excited and happy.

Tomorrow they will start the harvest. Soon there will be a meal of rice cooked with fish or duck. Or perhaps the duck will be roasted in the coals and the rice will be cooked with dried blueberries, for many of the people have just come from the country of the blueberries. It will be a big feast. There will be plenty for all.

The next morning the sun shows the rice lake in all its beauty. As far as the eye can see the rice stretches like a green island. Twice as tall as a man, the sturdy stalks stand with their roots in the shallow water and bend gracefully back and forth in the light breeze. Along the top two feet of each stalk the rice grains hang suspended from their small stems, ready to drop off at the least shaking. Thousands of ducks and geese are already there, gorging themselves on the almost limitless food. Clouds of blackbirds wheel overhead and then descend to the rice, bending it down, pecking and shattering the grains. The Indians know they must get their share before the birds and wind have stripped the stalks of the delicious seeds.

Quickly the canoes are made ready and the women push off. Only an occasional man or half-grown boy goes along, for this is traditionally woman's work. As long as the people can remember, it has been the women who went out each fall in the canoes to harvest the rice.

The rice stalks are so close together that it's impossible to paddle the canoe, so it's pushed with a forked pole. Two women go in each canoe, one to push with the pole from the back seat of the canoe, and one to knock the rice off the stalks into the canoe. This woman holds two beater sticks. With one she reaches out and bends a bunch of stalks over the canoe, with the other she beats the rice heads to knock the grains into the canoe. Back and forth across the lake they go in regular lines, each path next to the last, so as much of the grain can be gathered as possible. When the canoe is low in the water, heavy with the precious grain, the women push to shore and unload.

Clever as the women are, much of the grain drops down into the water and is lost. Some is too green yet, and stays on the stem even when the woman beats it. The Indian women try to get as much as they can, but their best efforts yield them only about one fourth of the total crop. This is an advantage to the rice. Like all wild seed plants the rice has developed a means of scattering its seeds so there will be new plants in the next generation. The wild rice has seeds that shatter easily when ripe. Each passing breeze, or perching bird knocks them off into the water where they remain until the next spring.

When the loads of rice reach shore there is more work for the women. The harvested rice is damp and slightly green. The women know that if they had waited until it was fully ripe and mature they would have reaped scarcely any, since most would have fallen into the water before they could have maneuvered the boat into place. This damp rice must now be dried, either in the sun or over a slow fire.

Some Indian tribes built low platforms of stout sticks and covered them with bark. The rice was laid on the bark; fire was kept burning underneath. There was just enough fire to dry the rice, but not enough to kindle the bark.

In other tribes the women stirred the rice in a basket with hot coals. The coals dried the rice, and were kept from scorching it or the basket by the stirring. Indian women had to know just how many coals and how much rice to use, or both rice and basket would be spoiled. In later years, after the rice-gathering tribes had met white people, the Indians traded for metal kettles. The rice could be put in the kettle over the fire and stirred with a paddle to dry it. This was much easier. It took skill, but not as much as the basket and coals method.

All this time the rice grains were still wrapped in their straw hulls. The roasting had cracked these hulls and loosened them. The rice was now ready for the men's part of the work. This was the hulling and threshing.

There were various methods of hulling among the different peoples. Some tribes spread the rice on skins laid out on the ground and beat it with sticks. Others dug a round shallow hole in the ground, covered the bottom with a clean skin and put the rice in the hole. Then a man or youth would step into the hole and dance up and down, pounding the hulls off the rice with his moccasined feet. This dancing was often done to the rhythm of a monotonous chant.

When the hulls were loosened it was woman's turn again. It was her job to separate the hulls and chaff from the kernels. This was done with a winnowing basket or tray, often made of birchbark. The rice and hulls were put in this wide shallow basket, and with deft motions and the help of the wind, the hulls slipped off the edge of the basket while the purple-gray grains stayed inside.

If you or I were to try this winnowing I am sure we would spill more grain than we would save. Each Indian woman had learned this skill from her mother or grandmother, and she in turn had learned it from her female relatives. It took much practice to do good winnowing. They were very clever at it. As the women shook and jiggled the shallow baskets, the hulls slipped off the edges as if by magic.

The day was far gone by the time all this work was done. In the meantime men or boys had been out on the lake to catch ducks and fish. They had built fires ready for the cooks. Everyone was ravenously hungry. They were waiting for the first feast of rice in several

Top left, woman ties wild rice from boat; top right, typical jacket worn when tying wild rice; bottom, field of wild rice tied in bunches to prevent shattering.

months. Now the women began the cooking. The good smells of food drifted along the lake shore and through the trees.

However, there was one thing more that had to be done. Before the feast could begin there must be prayers to the Great Spirit. The Indians knew that the Great Spirit had given them this wonderful rice food. Some Indian tribes sprinkled a little tobacco on the water in a ceremony of thankfulness. Others said their prayers at a thanksgiving feast where the Great Spirit was asked to watch over them during the harvest so that no storms would come until the precious grain was gathered. No one was allowed to eat any of the rice until after the ceremony.

There are many legends that tell how the Great Spirit gave the rice to his people.

One of these tells of the boy Wenibozho, who lived with his grandmother. She loved her grandson so much that she did everything she could to make him happy. Perhaps she did too much for him because one day she realized that he was lazy and selfish. He hadn't learned the lessons of living in a hard world or the skills that were necessary in the Indian's life. She wondered what would happen to him when she was no longer there to care for him.

"My son," she said, "since you will not learn your lessons here at home with me, you must go away. You must take a long journey through unknown forests. You must become used to the hardships of life."

Wenibozho had no choice, so he went out into the dark forest. There were many animals in the forest. However, Wenibozho could not catch any of them to eat because he had never learned to shoot an arrow or throw a spear. He became very hungry. As he wandered along, almost exhausted, some little bushes spoke to him.

"Sometimes they eat us," they said in low musical voices.

At first Wenibozho paid no attention to the bushes, but went on through the woods. Soon he heard them again.

"Sometimes they eat us."

Finally he stopped and said to the plants, "Whom are you talking to?"

When the plants told him they were talking to him he stooped and dug up one of them. He found that the plant had a long root that looked as if it would be good to eat. When he tasted it he found it was sweet and good. Since he was so hungry he dug many of the plants and ate the roots. In fact, he ate so many that he became very sick. For three days he lay there in the woods too sick to move.

At the end of the three days he felt better so he wandered on. As he went along many plants spoke to him but he paid no attention to them. Finally he found himself at the edge of a lake. As he stood there some of the grasses seemed to be waving at him. When he went closer he could hear them murmuring.

"Sometimes they eat us," they said in soft musical whispers.

Wenibozho looked carefully at a stalk of the grass and saw that its top was loaded with long seeds. Gathering some of the seeds he pulled off the hulls and found the kernels had a most pleasing taste.

"Oh, you are good," he said to the grass. "What are you called?"

"We are called manomin, or good berry," the grass told him.

This time Wenibozho ate and ate, enough to satisfy his hunger. The rice did not hurt him at all. When finally he went back to his grandmother, he took some of the manomin with him as a present for her. And ever after that, so the Indians say, they have had manomin to eat as one of their favorite foods.

The good berry has had many names besides the ones given it by the Indians. It was mentioned in reports by early explorers who called it wild rice, wild oats, squaw rice, water oats and many other variations. All told of the vast expanses of these fields that had to be neither planted nor tilled, but could be found ready and waiting for the harvester. Many mentioned the beauty of these watery fields made up of broad grassy blades and graceful waving spikes. They reported that the fields stretched for miles and furnished food for thousands of Indians each fall, as well as for millions of waterfowl. Fur trappers and explorers often traded with the Indians for supplies of the grain, which became one of the main parts of their diet. A cupful of the grain was said to make a meal for two.

For the hunter-gatherer people the gathering of the wild rice was a part of their yearly wanderings. They felt that it was a harvest given them by the gods, a time of food plenty, a time for rejoicing.

After the harvest at the lakes they moved their camps to the winter hunting grounds.

One writer, Edward Tanner, wrote in 1820, "One family ordinarily gathers about five bushels of rice. Those who are industrious sometimes gather twenty-five, although this is very rare."

Another writer reported that each family collected about twelve or fifteen bushels at a lake in Wisconsin. And he added, "They could gather more if they did not spend so much time feasting and dancing every day and night during the time they are here."

The women of some of the tribes worked out a clever method of getting a larger part of the grain before it fell off into the water. They came to the lake early, while the grain was still green, or in the milk stage. Then they went out in canoes and tied the stalks into bundles by wrapping the tops with heavy string.

First, of course, they had made the string out of fiber they had stripped from inner tree bark. Then in long winter evenings before the campfires they had twisted it together. It must have taken many evenings to twist the *two* to *six miles* of string that each family needed.

This wrapping of the stalks kept more of the grain from falling into the water than when it was left loose. Also it protected much of the grain from hungry birds. Each woman tied her bunches a certain way so that she would know which were hers, and she could come back and harvest them in a few weeks when the rice was ripe.

One early traveler reported, "The graceful bunches and regular rows are extremely pleasing to see."

Manomin, the good berry, was taken back to Europe by plant explorers in the early days of the settlement of North America. An attempt was made to get it started in the lakes of Sweden but this was not successful.

Linnaeus, the great Swedish botanist, who developed the system of naming plants, was given some manomin in 1753. He gave it the name of *Zizania*, and a second name of *aquatica*, since it grows only in water.

There are two kinds of Zizania. One, with broad strap leaves and needle-thin kernels, grows along many tidal rivers emptying into the Atlantic Ocean. Blackbirds and bobolinks, as well as many water fowl, feast on this Zizania each fall. The other kind of wild rice has narrower leaves and shorter, thicker kernels. It is found in the upper Mississippi valley and eastward along both sides of the Canadian border, in Minnesota, Wisconsin, Michigan, North and South Dakota, and the Canadian provinces of Manitoba and Ontario. Another Zizania grows in Japan, Formosa and eastern China. In Japan it is called "fruit-of-the-waterweed."

Manomin, or Zizania, is a seed plant, one of the large grass family. It is a distant cousin of both oats and true rice. Growing to a height of ten to twelve feet, the flower spike stands a couple of feet above the coarse grass leaves. The spike drips with the small green flowers which have pointed leaflike coverings but no true petals. The male flowers on the lower part of the spike open like tiny green bells with six yellow clappers, the stamens. From these stamens the wind blows the yellow pollen to other manomin plants.

On the upper part of the flower spike the female flowers open to show a much-branched stigma like a tiny feathery plume. One of the green coverings of the female flower has a long spike or awn covered with bristles. After the pollen reaches this stigma the two green halves close tightly and do not open again.

When the seeds are ripe they drop off into the water. They do not float as do the seeds of many water plants. The manomin seeds bury themselves in the mud with the help of the bristles on the awn. There they do not rot but stay alive until the following spring when they send up sprouts.

Many efforts have been made to plant the rice in other lakes, and other countries, and even to grow it domestically. Few of these have been successful. The manomin goes its own way and resists all efforts to make it into a tame plant. Its ways are those of wild plants. It drops its seeds when ripe at the least jarring. It does not ripen all at once as do most domesticated cereals, but over a period of a couple of weeks. To get the wild grains to grow where he plants it, the botanist has to imitate these wild ways. This means that the seeds cannot be stored dry as are wheat and oats, but must be kept wet and cold. Growing conditions must be similar to those of its home lakes.

The wild rice that's sold in the markets does not come from the farmer's fields but from the manomin lakes as it has for centuries.

Much of the wild rice is still harvested by Indians. Many Indian families still make a yearly trip to the rice lakes. There they camp as their ancestors did, enjoying the beauty of the fall and the company of friends and relatives. A few still parch the grain in battered pots, and dance the hulls off. However, most of the rice is not eaten or kept for winter, but is saved to sell to the white buyer who will process it in a modern mill. Gone also, is the custom of only women in the canoes for the gathering. Couples of men and women, or even two men, go out in the canoes or narrow plank boats to beat off the grain which has such a ready market.

White men, too, have entered the business of wild rice, particularly in the processing part. Also, an occasional white man can be seen driving a mechanical gatherer which scoops the wild grains into its tin mouths. However, some states, such as Wisconsin, prohibit the harvesting of wild rice by any mechanical means. The rice can only be gathered in small boats pushed by poles, and knocked into the boats with beater sticks in the traditional manner. Then, too, much of the wild rice grows on the various Indian reservations and can only be harvested by residents of these reservations.

If the old-time rice gatherers could come back, perhaps one of the strangest sights they would see would be big planes, like giant birds, landing on some of the northern rice lakes. They would watch astounded as Indians, canoes and supplies were unloaded from the birds. This is the method one large company has taken to get its hired Indian gatherers into some almost inaccessible lakes in the Canadian wilderness. There the harvesters camp until the harvest is over. Each plane has been rebuilt to carry a thousand pounds of rice at a load. Each Indian is paid so much per pound for the rice he gathers.

In some years a total of a million pounds of wild rice is harvested in the United States and Canada. But as with all wild crops the harvest is unpredictable. A bumper yield one year may be followed by a near failure the next. Experts say the wild rice crops usually go in cycles, a bountiful harvest every four years followed by two fair years and one near-failure.

After the rice is harvested it is taken to a modern mill, where the parching is done in big drums rotating over slow gas fires. The hulls are taken off by machine hullers instead of the dancing feet of men. Big mechanical shakers replace the jiggling bark trays of the old-time squaws, and power fans give blasts of air to carry away the hulls. This mill machinery is similar to that for true rice.

No matter how it is gathered or processed, *Zizania aquatica*, the good berry, is still a wild food. It is one link that still unites us with our hunter-gatherer ancestors.

CHAPTER 7

THE SCIENCE DETECTIVES AND THE FIRST FARMERS

For more than four hundred thousand years, all men, women and children lived as hunters and gatherers. Then something startling happened. It is so important in the history of the world that it has been called the *first agricultural revolution*.

Only a few stone-age people must have taken part in this first revolution. Yet the change they made in their way of life was the first step to bigger and better towns, to ancient cities and kingdoms.

Who were these clever people? Where did they live? How did they take this first giant step into civilization?

Scientists have been asking themselves these questions for many years. Only recently have they found the answers to some of them. These answers came from detective work. Patiently the science detectives followed one clue after another.

As in all good detective stories, some of the clues were strange indeed. One of the clues that led to Jarmo, the earliest stone-age village found so far, was a native cigarette lighter, called a *strike-a-light*.

Jarmo is located in Iraq about 150 miles north of Baghdad. To the people living in the small villages in that part of Iraq, Jarmo was just another low mound of reddish dirt on the edge of a steep bluff.

But archaeologists — science detectives hunting clues to ancient life — are suspicious of mounds of earth that look different from the hills around them. They know that these mounds are often the remains of ancient towns of mud-walled houses — towns that were lived in for hundreds of generations. And anyway, in the case of Jarmo, there was the strike-a-light.

Like all good detectives, archaeologists often play hunches. Dr. Robert Braidwood, of Chicago University, had a hunch that the first farming was done in the hill regions of the Middle East.

His hunch was something more than a wild guess. It was based on many facts he had learned from his studies and from expeditions or "digs," as archaeologists call them. He knew that early hunter-gatherer peoples used wild grains. They must have learned a great deal about these grains which they collected each year. He knew that wild wheat and barley still grow in the higher hills of Iraq and Iran, and probably have for hundreds of thousands of years. Eventually, he reasoned, someone must have had the bold idea of planting some of this grain and then waiting for the harvest.

Also, he thought the farming would have had to start where there was enough rainfall for a crop without irrigation. This also pointed to the hills of Iraq where even today crops can be grown without bringing water to the land.

Anyway, this was his hunch. Because of it he wanted to dig a likely mound in these hills and see if he could prove his theory. Just which mound to dig was the big question.

Many archaeologists have dug in the Near East. Many have found ancient cities of great wealth. Treasures of gold, jewels and rich carvings have been brought to museums in Europe and America. Dr. Braidwood was not interested in this kind of dig. He wanted information on the first farmers.

In his search for a likely mound, Dr. Braidwood first went to the Department of Antiquities of Iraq, where the government has scientists who study the ancient relics of their country. The head of the department talked about several likely spots, and then told Dr. Braidwood about Jarmo and the strike-a-light.

One of the men from his department, the director said, had been on a trip to a certain village. He asked the Sheikh of the village if he knew of any place in his locality where there were signs that ancient people had once lived there.

The Sheikh shook his head. "No," he said. "I am sorry. I know of no such place. But will you have a cigarette?" He handed the official a cigarette. Then he took out his strike-a-light (a piece of flint rock, a twisted bit of steel to hit it with, and some fuzz to catch the spark).

As his cigarette was being lighted the official gave a start. "Pardon me, but would you mind if I looked at your piece of flint?"

The Sheikh looked puzzled, but politely handed over the stone.

The official examined the flint from which the spark had been struck. "Where did this come from?" he asked. "I am greatly interested in it."

"It's only a piece of flint which I picked up on a hill a few miles from my village," the Sheikh explained. "There are many of them on this hill. If you wish, I will show you."

There were indeed many pieces of flint on the hill. They were scattered all around on top of the ground in the dried grass.

"I don't think these are just ordinary stones," the official said. "I think they were left by the ancients." He gathered a collection of the pieces and sent them back to his department.

When the flints were examined by experts they agreed that he was right. The pieces of stone were broken blades and scraps of flint left by stone-age men in their toolmaking. The piece of flint used by the Sheikh in his strike-a-light had been used by another man several thousand years before. The lighter was part modern and part stone-age.

When Dr. Braidwood heard this story he went to look at the Jarmo mound. He also examined other sites where he might start his dig; but always his mind came back to Jarmo.

"I like that place," he said. "Let's ask for permission to make a test dig."

The permission was secured and a short trench was dug as a test. Even though this test showed interesting artifacts, there were many difficulties to be overcome before Dr. Braidwood and his staff could begin their real dig. Thousands of dollars had to be found to pay for the fares to Iraq, to hire the native diggers, to buy the food and the many things that would be needed while the members of the expedition lived at the site. Then they had to find the right people to take along, people who had special skills as well as science education. For instance, it was most important to have someone who could repair jeeps, since at Jarmo there wouldn't be a garage just around the corner to keep their cars in repair.

Also, there were no houses at Jarmo. Before they could settle down to digging, the scientists had to have some place to live. It was decided to have a house built at Jarmo out of bricks made from mud and straw, then baked in the sun. This is the material often used for houses in this area where timber is scarce. It is a way of house-building that has come down from ancient times. Only the doors, windows and roof would be made of more modern materials.

Early one fall the expedition arrived at Jarmo. The house was there waiting for them. It's thick mud walls and metal roof covered with dirt would protect them from the cold of the winter and the heat of summer. They moved in and spread rugs on the hard-packed mud floors. They whitewashed the room walls, and built board shelves for storage. They even installed a shower and sink. The women of the expedition covered the big dining table with red oil-cloth, and tacked bright travel posters on the walls.

Finally, the digging started. The dirt began to come out of the holes; and the pieces of stone, bone and pottery were picked from the dirt and cleaned. Many of the native diggers were experts. They had dug for other expeditions. They were as anxious to find relics of the ancients as were the science detectives. By the number of artifacts they were finding, everyone could see that people had lived at Jarmo for a long time. But what kind of people were they? How had they lived? And when?

The science detective never knows what he will find in one of his digs. Dr. Braidwood was looking for knowledge of ancient life but especially he was hoping for clues of the *first* farmers, the people who had changed their way of life from the hunting-gathering of their ancestors.

Not in one month or even in one season are such questions answered. Tons of dirt have to be scooped out of the mound. Thousands of little pieces of stone, bone and pottery have to be separated from the ordinary rocks. As many as 1,500 pieces of chipped stone might be found in one day; a hundred thousand in a season's dig. Each one had to be cleaned, examined, marked with ink and recorded in a book.

The tools and other things left by the most recent Jarmo people were nearest the top. Even they had been stone-age people. They had had pottery dishes and cooking pots, but no metal of any kind. The farther down in the mound the diggers reached, the more ancient the people. There were sixteen different levels of living that could be distinguished at Jarmo. It was the bottom level that everyone was waiting for. Here it was that the first farmers had lived if Dr. Braidwood's theory was right.

As the diggers carefully removed the dirt they could see the houses the ancients had lived in. All their houses had been made of mud, mud walls strengthened with straw and built up in layers a little at a time. Each layer had been allowed to dry and harden before more mud was added. Walls like these are built even today in the villages of Iraq.

Houses made of mud are fine and sturdy during the dry part of the year. However, with the hard winter rains and wind the walls get wet and often start to crumble. The owners try to prevent this by building wide overhanging roofs. Also they repair any damage as soon as they can but this is difficult when it is raining. Sometimes the walls slip so much there is nothing a family can do except leave their home and move in with relatives. The average life of one of these mud-walled houses is only about fifteen years.

The tendency of such houses to crumble is the reason for mounds such as Jarmo. Ancient people lived in the mud houses which gradually settled into piles of dirt. Other people came along and built new houses in the same place. After centuries this process gradually raised the level of the whole town. If you visited the Middle East today you could see some of the modern cities with their older central parts sitting on top of ancient mounds.

Even when houses have crumbled to a pile of dirt and other houses

Jarmo excavation, stone foundation of first level in center of picture

have been built on top of them, there is some record of the former buildings. Careful digging can trace the old walls because the wall dirt is harder than the dirt that has slumped around it. This is what Dr. Braidwood's workers did. By careful scraping they found the lower part of the walls and even the rooms in which the ancients had lived. They found the floors they had walked on, made of mud smoothed over layers of reeds.

The crumbling, slumping dirt had also buried many *things* that the people had used. From these things the science detectives tried to picture the way the people had lived.

68

They found pieces of stone knives sharp enough to cut meat or whittle a stick. There were flint scrapers that could have cleaned the flesh from an animal hide so it could be tanned and used for protection against the cold. There were borers that might have made holes in wood or bone. Then there were platters and bowls. Many of these were carefully made out of stone, the result of many weeks of skillful pounding and rubbing. The bowls were handsome with smooth curved sides and rounded edges. Other bowls were fashioned of clay. But the Jarmo people hadn't learned how to fire clay or glaze it, so their pottery wasn't very good.

Bone awls were found, and needles with an eye for thread. This showed that the Jarmo women must have sewed some kind of clothing. And there were bracelets of marble, and beads — lots of beads. Perhaps the men made them for their women.

But what had the Jarmo people eaten? What kind of food had the women served their men and children in the clay or stone bowls? Remnants of food are apt to be scarce in an archaeological dig. Answers as to what people ate thousands of years ago come only from piecing together many tiny clues.

The most common food clue was the snail shells, piles and piles of them. Then there were acorn hulls and shells of other kinds of nuts which must have been gathered in the woods. Neither of these clues pointed to any kind of farming.

There were the bones of animals which must have been eaten as meat. A scientist with special training examined these. He said there were bones of sheep, pig, gazelle, cattle and dog, plus a scattering of other animals. Bones of sheep and goats were the most common. The goats and dogs were probably tame, the expert said, since their bones differed slightly from the wild ones still found in that part of Iraq.

Other clues to the Jarmo people's food were flat hollowed-out mortar stones and the manos for grinding. These might have meant that the people were still seed-collectors, although it seemed doubtful

Animal figurines of clay found at Jarmo

that the population of Jarmo, estimated at about one hundred fifty people, could have collected enough seeds to feed themselves.

The clues to the story were getting warmer now, but they still hadn't told the answer.

Interesting finds were narrow strips of flint, sharpened on one edge. The other edge was thicker and had crude tar on it as if it had been fastened to something. In one find there were four of these sharp-edged flints lying near each other, and they fitted together in an arc. The sharp edges were shiny, as stone knives get when they have been used to cut some kind of grass. (The sandlike silica in the grass makes them shine.) Clearly these four pieces had been fastened into a piece of wood and used as a sickle. Did the Jarmo people cut grain that they had raised, or were the sickles only used to cut reeds that floored the houses? Reeds also would have made the stone knives shiny.

Then one day a scientist noticed some queer marks on a piece of hardened clay.

"Look what I found," he shouted. "Those marks must have been made by straw that was pressed into the mud when it was wet." He pointed at the tiny marks. "And look at the thicker places at the top. They look like impressions of some kind of grain."

Later many other molded impressions of straw and spikes of grain were found. And then one day a really important discovery was made.

One of the scientists was examining the small objects that a native digger had sifted out of the dirt he had removed. His finds were lying on a piece of hand-woven cloth which he had brought from his home.

As the two men leaned over the bright-colored cloth, the digger pointed with his dusty finger at a small pile of little black crumbs. "Look," he said.

The scientist took the crumbs into his palm and turned them over and over. Then he took a hand microscope from his pocket and examined them carefully.

"Good," he said. "These are good. Wonderful." He carried the black crumbs back to show his fellow scientists. "Look," he said. "I think these are kernels of grain, either wheat or barley. Wish we had our Danish friend, the expert, here. He could tell us."

The picture of the early Jarmo people was getting clearer now. More kernels of grain were found. And better than that, some of them turned out to be different from the wild wheat and barley that still grow in the higher hills. Some of the kernels were from grain that had been changed by man, grain that had been cultivated for long enough time — perhaps centuries — to lose some of its wildness.

The native wheats and barleys all have brittle stems. They break apart when they are ripe. Native grasses have to have ways to scatter their seeds, otherwise they will die out. Plants tamed by man don't need this scattering ability any more; men will do the scattering for them. In fact, men don't like grains that shatter at the first touch. Too much of the grain is lost before it can be harvested, if the seeds fall off easily. So man gradually chooses for planting the kinds that shatter least.

The Jarmo wheats and barleys were on the way to being changed and tamed. Some of them had heads as brittle as the wild kinds, others had stems not so easily broken, according to Dr. Hans Halbaek, the Danish scientist who examined the grains and the impressions in the clay. Others of the grains were similar to a primitive kind of wheat, called *emmer*, still grown in some parts of the world for cattle feed.

Other finds, too, seemed to point to the conclusion that the Jarmo people were beginning farmers, along with some collecting and hunting. There were, for instance, carefully made stone tools that could have been used for hoes. Also there were hollowed-out hearths in the floors and a few real ovens.

"I doubt if early people such as those at Jarmo baked bread," Dr. Braidwood said. "They probably parched their grain, then pounded it and made it into mush. Maybe they chewed some of it dry, as we eat popcorn."

The parching or roasting was probably to loosen the hulls of the wheat and barley in those early days. Jarmo grain, unlike modern wheat, would have been difficult to hull without parching. The grains found in the dig thousands of years later were preserved because they had been parched a little too much. Like the modern housewife who occasionally burns a pan of food, some ancient Jarmo woman must have been careless or busy. Maybe the baby cried and she went to pick him up. While she was gone some of the precious wheat burned.

Think what it must have meant to these wandering people to have a permanent home at last. Now the women and children did not have to trail behind their men from one camping place to another, carrying their few possessions on their backs. Now they could have more things, and heavier ones — stone mortars and grinding stones that could sit in a corner and wait for the user, heavy stone bowls instead of light easily carried baskets. They could have skin blankets for winter that didn't have to be lugged around all summer long.

More important than these things was the food supply. These people could have more food, enough to last a year, or perhaps two years if the harvest was extra good. With permanent homes, this food could be stored and kept safe from hungry animals and wandering strangers.

Now there was a little leisure once in a while, time to sit in the sun and perhaps tell stories to the children. Or there was time to fashion small objects out of clay such as those found at Jarmo, little clay pigs, lions and sheep.

Hunter-gatherer people do not have much leisure time. As Dr. Braidwood says, "Before the agricultural revolution most men must have spent their waking moments looking for their next meal, except when they were gorging themselves after a great hunt."

Later, men were to use this leisure to develop the plow and the wheel and to learn skills such as weaving and the smelting of metals from ores.

How many years ago was it when Jarmo was a village of a couple of dozen mud houses? How many suns of summer have given way to the cold rains of winter since the woman left her parching job for a little while and burned the wheat?

Dating a prehistoric site is always tricky. There are radiocarbon dates for Jarmo as well as other evidence. Dr. Braidwood feels that, all things considered, the reasonable date for the agricultural revolution and Jarmo is about nine thousand years ago.

CHAPTER 8

AMERICA'S MYSTERY PLANT–CORN

Corn is one of the most important plants that stand between mankind and starvation. It is one of the most efficient traps we have to catch the energy from the sun in a few chemical steps and store it in food — food which gives us energy to live and operate our bodies.

Corn is grown in both American continents, from central Canada to the southern part of South America. It is cultivated in every one of the fifty states of the United States and is the number one plant in our economy. We are all familiar with it. Yet of all the strange stories in the history of mankind none is more mystifying than that of corn.

The threads of the story weave in and out from a sack of fluffy white popcorn bought in a movie theater, to a stalk of corn made of solid gold, to a dusty cave in New Mexico.

Scientists shrug their shoulders and say bluntly that corn is a "botanical monstrosity." There is no other plant like it in the plant kingdom.

Corn is a grass, one of the more than five thousand kinds of grasses in the world. Most grasses have seeds that are light and easily scattered by the wind. A few, like wild wheat and oats, have heavier seeds, but have brittle stems that break off and fall to the ground, or the seeds are brushed off into the fur of animals.

The seeds of corn are tightly attached to a rigid cob. Furthermore, they are securely wrapped in several thicknesses of tough leaf sheaths.

If a cob of corn ever did fall to the ground — which does not happen often — several hundred seeds would lie together until spring when many of them would sprout. The competition among the young for food and water at that one spot would be so great that few would have enough nourishment to grow to maturity and bear ears of corn. As a consequence there would be little or no seed for the following year.

Thus, corn is wholly dependent on man for its survival. It is man who must plant a few of the several hundred grains from the ear in one spot in the ground, so that the corn can reach maturity and bear seed for the next year.

Scientists point out that no plant could have survived long in the wild under such conditions. They say that such a plant would have died out long before man came on the scene.

But corn didn't die out. What then is the explanation?

These same scientists say that corn must have come from something else. It must have come from a combination of two or more other plants, or from a wild ancestor corn that could scatter its seeds. It must have come from some plant that did not have its hundreds of seeds wrapped and fastened tightly to a rigid stalk. Where then is the wild corn and what does it look like?

Plant explorers have been looking for this wild corn plant for many years. They have climbed high mountains and crossed swift rivers. They have gone far from civilization to places where native tribes live who have never seen a white man. They have found wild wheats, wild barleys and wild oats.

Nowhere have they found a wild corn that was truly wild. The primitive corns they found had been planted and tended by some native tribe. And all looked like corn, with ears held tightly to a stalk.

Other scientists took another approach to the problem. They studied the history of corn. This led them through many devious trails.

As far as written history is concerned corn is not very old. Nowhere in the writings of ancient Egypt or Babylonia is there any mention of corn. Early Greeks or Romans did not write of it, and the corn spoken of in the Bible, scholars tell us, is a translation of the Hebrew word for wheat. There is no mention of such a grain in the 5,000-year-old Chinese manuscripts or in the almost equally old sagas of India.

Evidently, there was no corn in Africa or Asia. Nor was there any corn grown in early England or Europe.

The first Europeans to see corn were two of the men who went with Christopher Columbus on his first voyage to America.

It was early in November of 1492. The three little ships which had fought their way across the Atlantic were at last anchored in a snug harbor on the north side of Cuba.

Columbus was sure he had reached Asia, and he decided to send a party inland to the nearest city to pay tribute to the king who he thought would be there. He chose two men from his ships and sent a friendly Indian with them as a guide.

They started on a Friday morning, carrying presents for the Indians, with instructions from Columbus, the Admiral, to return in six days.

They returned sooner than expected, in only half of the six days, loaded with presents which the Indians had given them. They showed the presents and told of the wonderful things they had seen. There was a town with fifty houses and a thousand inhabitants, they said. Many of the people were holding in their mouths little rolls of dried leaves. They lighted these rolls at one end and drew the smoke into their lungs. Almost as an afterthought the visitors mentioned a grain which the Indians called "maize," and which they ate roasted or boiled.

Columbus was looking for spices and gold, and for a route to Asia. He was no botanist, and even if he had been it is doubtful if he would have been much interested in the strange food plant. Certainly he would not have realized that this plant represented more gold than his ships could have carried back to Europe in many voyages.

In his second voyage Columbus found more of the strange food plant. It was growing on all the islands of the West Indies and wherever he touched the mainland of Central and South America. His brother, Diego, told of one place in Central America where he traveled for eighteen miles through fields of this maize.

A quantity of the strange grain must have been taken back to Europe by someone who came with Columbus on his second voyage because it is mentioned in a Spanish book by Peter Martyr, dated 1511.

Soon after this, the famous early botanist, Leonhard Fuchs, included a picture of the corn plant in his book about plants. A few people began to grow corn in their gardens as a botanical curiosity. As yet no one in Europe realized the importance of corn in the New World.

What kind of corn was it that the Spanish invaders found? The picture in Fuchs' book shows four stalks of corn with ears wrapped securely in husks. The ears are fastened about half way up the stalks, with tassels far above them at the top of the plants. They look surprisingly like stalks of corn growing in a Kansas cornfield. Another Spanish writer spoke of the corn ear which was longer than his palm and as thick as a man's arm.

Scientists are forced to conclude that this corn was neither primitive nor wild when the Spanish first saw it, but had been under cultivation for a long time by the inhabitants of Central and South America.

Later explorations of other parts of America tell a similar story. As Europeans scattered over the Americas, they saw corn. The French found it in Canada, the English in what is now the United States, the Spanish and Portuguese in South America.

In the lush tropics corn grew twenty feet high. In the Andes mountains at ten thousand feet elevation it was sometimes less than two feet. But it was still corn, man-planted and man-tended.

Most of the Indians in the Americas — except those in California and the frigid north and south — had their patches of corn. Altogether they had not only one variety of corn, but all the main kinds of corn that we find today.

Modern agricultural scientists have made biological crosses to produce much bigger ears with many more grains on each ear. But they have not produced one new kind of corn that was not in the Americas when Columbus arrived.

What of the early civilizations in America, the Mayas, the Aztecs, the Incas and their ancestors? What did they eat that gave them energy to build the huge pyramids, some of them 200 feet high with temples on top constructed of massive stone blocks?

Building blocks on top of our big buildings are lifted by engines which are run by energy that comes from coal, oil or water power. However, in the time of the Mayas and Incas, man had not learned to tap the energy sources stored in the earth. The mighty projects of the ancients were all made by human hands. Each stone taken to the top of a temple in Mayan times was lifted by energy that came from man's muscles, which were powered by food he had eaten.

Scientists who have studied the ancient civilizations of South and Central America have concluded that they could not have flourished if it had not been for the corn plant. They point out that each great civilization has been based on some cereal food. Egypt was built on wheat; ancient China and India on rice. Primitive foods, gathered in the woods and fields, simply would not have supported enough population to build the cities and towns that were great when Europe was young.

The Americas had no wheat or rice, so the civilization of the Mayas and the Incas, as well as that of early Peru, was based on another cereal plant, the corn plant. Corn, of course, was supplemented by other foods such as beans and squash, as well as a little meat. It was corn, however, that was eaten three times a day, as it is in Mexico today, that constituted the "bread" of the people.

What kind of corn was this? scientists ask themselves. And where did these people get this corn?

There are plenty of answers to the first question. Scientists have found hundreds of ears of corn molded in clay decorating pottery vessels made by the Mayas of Central America more than a thousand years ago. Ears of corn are carved in stone on some of the sculptures that stand deserted in the jungles. Real ears of corn are found in graves and an occasional corn popper made of pottery, which shows they had popcorn and knew how to pop it. There are also pottery ears of corn made for the children to play with.

The Incas conquered many other Indian tribes and built a civilization in Peru that flourished five hundred years later than the Mayas. Among their mighty projects was a temple to the sun god at Cuzco.

This temple was surrounded by a garden in which all the plants were made of silver or gold. There were golden flowers blooming under trees of gold and silver. Birds of gold sat in the branches and golden lizards lay underneath. There were even golden life-size llamas, South American animals that resemble a camel, though smaller and without humps. There was also a large cornfield, every stalk of which was made of pure gold.

The first Spaniard to see this gleaming garden must have stared in awe, for even the ground was pebbled with gold nuggets. One of the Spaniards wrote that the stalks and ears of the golden corn were made so solidly that storms did not damage them.

The greedy conquerors from Spain made short work of this garden. Most of it was speedily melted down into bars to be taken back to Spain. There is little left to remind the world of its marvels except mention here and there in books and letters as men remembered afterward the things they had seen and wrote down their memories. There is, however, a receipt in existence for one of the golden cornstalks, which testifies that the stalk had three leaves and two ears of 14-karat gold. Its weight was certified as ten marks and six and four-eighths ounces, or more than five pounds of gold in that one cornstalk.

Many scientists have searched the inscriptions for a hint of where corn came from originally. Who first found the wild plant and tamed it?

The Mayas' answer is simple. It was given them by the gods.

Maize was once hidden under a great pile of rock, they say. It was found by the ants, who went under the rock and began to carry away the corn. Each ant took one corn grain on his back. The Fox, always curious, saw the ants and tasted one of the grains. He found it was good. Soon some of the other animals as well as man saw what the ants were doing. Everyone wanted some of the new food but nobody but the ants could get any, because of the big mountain of rock.

Finally, man asked the rain gods to help him. Three of the rain gods hammered the rock with lightning and thunderbolts, but the mountain was too strong for them. Then man asked the oldest of the rain gods, the big chief. At first he said no, but after they had begged him many times he consented to try. Before he began he sent the woodpecker to sound the rock with his bill and find the weakest spot. Then he sent his fiercest weapon. Thunder rolled among the mountains louder than anyone had ever heard. Mighty bolts of lightning shot from the sky and the smell of fire filled the air. Finally, with one last gigantic crash the mountain was split and corn lay there before man.

Ever since that time, the Mayas say, man has been grateful to the gods for the gift of corn. He gives thanks and offerings whenever he plants or reaps the sacred grain.

Other American peoples have equally picturesque legends about the origin of corn. None of them is much help to the scientist who is searching for the original corn plant.

Some scientists have maintained that corn is a cross between two other wild grasses that are botanically a little like corn. Other scientists say no. Corn must have come from a wild corn plant even though it has never been found.

Scientists have recently uncovered several clues to the solution of the mystery.

The first of these was found, like many of the clues to ancient man, in a cave. Known as Bat Cave, it is located in the state of New Mexico. Like Danger Cave, it is on the shores of an ancient lake, now dried into a flat plain. The cave is 165 feet above what was once the bottom of the lake.

The people who lived in the cave weren't very good housekeepers from the modern standpoint. When they ate meat, probably by gnawing it from the bone, they didn't throw the bone outside but tossed it back of them inside the cave. When the women were hulling seeds, or shelling nuts, they were not careful to throw the shells outside either.

These things mixed with leaves they had brought in for bedding, and dirt that blew in from outside. This trash accumulated and packed down hard on the floor of the cave. It made a new and higher floor, and other people came and lived in the cave. Their children came, and their children's children. Probably like many Indian groups they lived outdoors under temporary shelters when the weather was good and only came into the cave in the winter when it was cold or rainy.

This is the kind of cave that scientists like to dig, because usually there were other things lost in the leaves and dirt besides bones and nut shells. Often there are arrowheads, and stone knife blades, as well as baskets, pottery and woven string nets which the women made. In the case of Bat Cave, the scientists calculated that the six feet of compressed trash represented 3,000 years of living.

On the very bottom layer there was something that had never been seen by modern man before. There were tiny cobs of corn — primitive corn — the kind that these people either planted or found growing wild. The cobs were about the size of a penny, and when they were sent to the radiocarbon laboratory their age was found to be 5,600 years.

Altogether, there were 766 corncobs found in the dirt taken from the cave floor. In the more recent layers (those nearer the top) the cobs were larger, showing that successive generations had been able to raise better corn than their forefathers.

Not a single cob in all the 766 had any kernels left on it. This showed that the ancients, although they were poor housekeepers, were careful workmen when it came to shelling corn. However, they did drop an occasional grain of corn, for 125 loose kernels were found by the scientists as they sifted the dirt from the cave.

The kernels from the tiny cobs of the lower layer were small and hard, like popcorn. In other layers the corn raised by later peoples had bigger grains.

The important thing about Bat Cave excavations, the scientists

Right, several kinds of corn: (1) pop-corn with pointed grains; (2) pod corn, each grain enclosed in its own husk; (3 and 4) corn from mountains of Peru, more primitive than (5) hybrid dent corn, raised by most farmers in the United States. Below, hybrid corn a few weeks old, six inches high.

Field of hybrid corn

say, is that corn was corn, even 5,000 years ago, and must have been cultivated by man.

Small primitive cobs of corn have also been found in another cave, La Perra, in Mexico not far below the U.S. border. In this cave a child must have died while the parents were living there. The tiny body was buried in the dirt at the back of the cave. So that their child would not be hungry on the long trip which they thought it must take to the other world, they tied three cobs of corn together with string and laid them near the body.

The corncobs found in these two caves not only told the scientists that man had been raising corn nearly six centuries ago, but they also showed what kind of corn they raised. By studying the cobs from Bat Cave the scientists decided it must have been both popcorn and *pod corn*. In other words, it had small pointed grains that popped when heated, and also each of these little grains was enclosed in a separate leafy wrapping.

Pod corn, which is not often seen in this country, occurs once in a while as a freak in fields of corn. In some places it is treasured by the Indians, who think it is good magic or lucky.

One of the scientists, Dr. P. C. Mangelsdorf, who has been studying and raising experimental patches of corn for many years, decided to try crossing some of this pod corn with a primitive kind of popcorn. After several years of experiments, and many failures, he succeeded in producing a tiny ear of corn which looked quite similar to those found in Bat Cave.

This doesn't prove, Dr. Mangelsdorf says, that primitive man produced his corn in this way. Since corn, like people, inherits characteristics from its ancestors, the experiment proves that ancient Bat Cave corn must have had some of the traits that are now in some types of modern corn. It also proves that modern corn could have come from such ancient corn as that in Bat Cave.

Corn apparently had lost the ability to scatter its seeds even back in those days. Man in America, like man in Asia, had taken the first steps toward farming and away from merely wandering in the woods to collect food.

Early gardeners, probably women, must have combined these two ways of securing food. The women raised a small patch of corn while the men were out hunting. Also many seeds and nuts, as well as roots were collected to eat with the corn. In fact, study of the different layers of soil from La Perra Cave says just this thing.

Soils from the different layers were examined to determine what proportion of each food was eaten by the people. In the lower or older layers most of the food came from the wild plants and animals. In the upper layers more food came from plants in the garden plots, from corn and beans and squash.

Neither of these caves answered the question, how old is corn?

The nearest thing to an answer came from a hole in Mexico City a few years ago. There, a hole was drilled 200 feet deep as part of the preparations for the foundation of a skyscraper. A scientist who examined the dirt under a microscope found fossil pollens. Corn, which has the largest pollen of any known grass, was easily recognized. It looked identical with pollen from modern corn. When geologists estimated the age of the strata at the bottom of the hole they said, "Eighty thousand years."

This proves that when man came to America — probably from Asia via the Bering Strait — he found corn already there ahead of him. What this corn looked like, the fossil pollens could not tell. The final answer must wait for more research. However, we know for sure that it was a lucky thing for both ancient and modern man that there was a corn plant in America that could once scatter its seeds.

Ancient Peruvian pot with ear of maize molded on it

CHAPTER 9

SICK SAILORS AND HUNGRY ANIMALS—VITAMIN C

People had been eating plants and their seeds for many thousand years before they learned anything about the science of nutrition, or how an animal or plant takes in and utilizes its food. Indeed, the main effort of most of the human race throughout history has been to find enough to eat. All foods were believed to be equally nutritious; they only seemed different. Hence if foods tasted and smelled good they must be wholesome.

This lack of knowledge of the food needs of the body often brought tragedies like that which happened to the men who sailed with the French explorer, Jacques Cartier.

In the sixteenth century the great adventure that young men dreamed of was a sea voyage across the Atlantic Ocean, to a new world that seemed as far from Europe then as the moon seems to us now. The trip was filled with many dangers and only the young and strong dared try it.

Still, there was never any trouble getting men to sign on the ships that were being outfitted. Hadn't Spanish ships crossed the southern waters and come back loaded with gold, silver and pearls — enough to make every man that went along rich for life?

Of course, the Spanish had staked out the southern crossing and that part of the new world for their own. However, there seemed to be no reason why the northern part of this wonderful new land shouldn't be as rich. So the French and English kept trying to find the cities of gold as well as a route to the Orient. Jacques Cartier was one of these.

It was the year 1535. Cartier had led an expedition to the northeastern coast of North America the summer before and had returned, but without any gold. This time he proposed to stay longer and search farther.

The ships started from St. Malo, France, in April and crossed the Atlantic in three weeks. They explored several rivers that emptied into the Atlantic and then sailed up the St. Lawrence as far as the Indian town of Hochelaga. The savages there dressed in skins and lived in houses. They raised corn, beans and pumpkins, but they had no gold or pearls. However, one of the Indians told the captain of a wonderful place farther on where the people wore clothes made of wool even as the Frenchmen did. He declared these people had great stores of gold and copper. Cartier decided to spend the winter in the New World and continue his search the next spring.

The Indians that lived near the harbor were friendly as long as they were given enough presents. Such things as knives, hatchets and beads delighted them. In return they gave the sailors game which they had killed in the woods with their bows and arrows, and fish they caught in the rivers.

Then it began to snow. Almost continuously the white flakes fell, covering everything and making it impossible to fish and hard to catch any game animals. As winter deepened the snow piled to more than four feet, and the ice thickened.

The savages were having trouble feeding themselves now, so they did not bring as much food as formerly to trade for beads and trinkets. The men in the icy ships — all young men, mostly in their twenties — cut their rations and prepared to last out the winter on such foods as they still had in storage, plus what little they could get from the savages.

Probably their supplies were mostly salted beef and hard bread made from white flour. The bread may have been mouldy — it often was when kept in the damp holds of ships.

Then began a very bad time. The men didn't like to talk of it afterward, but two wrote down their memories to warn others how terrible it had been. You can read what they wrote in musty books, now yellowed with age.

The first hint of danger came from the Indian lodges. As one writer says, "In the month of December we received warning that the pestilence had broken out among the people."

When Cartier heard about this sickness among the Indians he was immediately alarmed. The Indians must be kept away from the ships, he said, or they might bring the disease to the sailors. He issued an order that no Indian was to come in or near the three vessels.

In spite of this precaution men on the ships began to get sick. It was a terrible disease that none of them had seen before. It affected their legs and arms so that they couldn't work or even walk.

As winter lengthened and the snows piled higher, more and more men became sick. Strong men who had been able to climb into the rigging of a ship during the fiercest storm became as helpless as babies.

"The disease," wrote one of the men, "spread among the three ships to such an extent that in the middle of February, of the 110 men forming our company, there were not ten in good health so that no one could aid the other."

In their weakness they began to worry about the savages who surrounded them. If the Indians were to find out how helpless the sailors were they might attack the ships.

These young men who never had known fear before in their lives became terribly afraid. If the savages attacked, the sick men in bed and the few who were still able to walk would be helpless to stop them. The Indians could easily capture the ships and take everything.

In this desperate situation the Captain figured out a plan. If the Indians didn't know how helpless the sailors were they probably wouldn't attack. He decided to try to deceive the Indians. Whenever any Indians came in the vicinity of the ships the Captain forced a few of his sick men to walk on shore with him where the Indians could see them. Then he would yell at these men and whip them with a stick, pretending that he was driving them back to the ship where they were supposed to be at work. Inside the ships he would have the rest of the sick men pound on the boards with hammers, as if they were calking the seams.

Whether the Indians believed this or not, at least they didn't attack. Perhaps they were too busy with their own troubles.

As winter dragged on neither medicine nor prayers helped the sailors. The sick became worse, and more than twenty died. The crew was too weak to dig into the frozen ground so the dead men were buried under the snow.

One day the Captain, who somehow managed to avoid the sickness, was walking on the shore. He met one of the Indians, Dom Agaya, whom he had seen ten or twelve days before with legs sore and badly swollen from the pestilence. Incredibly now, Dom was walking as if he had never been sick.

The Captain pointed to Dom's legs. "How did you get rid of the sickness?"

He was cured by a tree, Dom said. He had taken the leaves from a certain tree and boiled them in water, then swallowed the juice.

The Captain could hardly believe that such a simple thing would cure this terrible plague. However, he decided to try it.

"Show us the tree," he ordered. "One of my servants has lately become sick with this affliction."

Dom sent two Indian women out into the woods with the Captain. They pulled some branches and bark from a hemlock tree and showed how they mashed them in water and then boiled them.

The Captain took this dirty greenish mixture back to the ship and told the sick men to try it.

Most of the men thought the whole thing was useless. How could a few boiled evergreen needles cure a disease that had already killed twenty-five men and was certainly going to kill that many more? Most of them turned over painfully in their bunks and refused to drink the unpleasant-looking mess.

Only a couple of sailors agreed to try it. Incredibly, after they had taken it a few days they began to feel better. In a few more days these men who had almost given up hope, were entirely well and strong.

Then, all the sick men wanted some of the marvelous medicine. Men were sent into the forest to bring back more branches. As one writer told it:

"There was such a press for the medicine that they almost killed each other to have it first; so that in less than eight days a whole tree as large and as tall as any I ever saw was used up." And he concluded, "All who were willing to use it, recovered health and strength."

Neither Cartier nor his men knew what had caused the disease from which they had so miraculously recovered, or why the needles from a tree cured them. In fact, it wasn't until the twentieth century, nearly four hundred years later, that the mystery was explained.

As late as 1900 scientists thought that if people ate enough protein such as is found in meat, milk and eggs, the rest of the body's needs would be automatically supplied from any kind of food. Even when Dr. Eijkman out in Java showed that his hens fed on polished white rice developed the same weak legs and then died, as did the sick prisoners in the jail who ate the white milled rice, nutrition experts still talked only of three basic foods.

They were very scientific about these basic nutrients. They laughed at the old-fashioned idea that all foods were composed of a single food principle. No, indeed, they said. All foods were made up of one or more of the three basics. The protein was needed for growth and repair of body cells, the fats and the starchy or sweet carbohydrates for body energy. The scientists did grudgingly admit that a pinch of minerals was probably useful as well. Everything else, they said, was taste and flavor, mere extras that were not necessary for life and health.

Looking back it seems incredible that the lessons of history were not better understood. There were certainly plenty of horrible examples on record. Besides the twenty-five men of Cartier's expedition who died of the pestilence — later called scurvy — thousands of other sailors had perished from the same disease. Admiral Sir Richard Hawkins of the British Navy wrote in 1593 that 10,000 seamen had died from scurvy within his own personal experience. When Vasco da Gama sailed around the Cape of Good Hope in 1489, 100 of his men died from scurvy out of a crew of 160. And on one occasion it was said that a Spanish galleon was found floating with an entire crew of dead men as a result of this dread disease.

It is not only sailors and eaters of rice in the Orient that history tells about. In the siege of Paris by the Germans in 1870, it was particularly the babies that were affected. As the ring of soldiers tightened around the city, the food for people inside became scarcer and scarcer. There was almost no milk, and mothers began to be terribly frightened for their little ones. The wail of the hungry infants could be heard day and night.

Then the babies began to die. As the number of small coffins increased, the scientists were begged for help. Since milk was only protein, fats and carbohydrates plus a few minerals, couldn't these eminent men make an artificial milk?

The scientists tried to manufacture some milk. They worked hard and furiously at it. They concocted a pale white liquid of fat, sugar and protein which they said should be every bit as good as real milk. But the babies kept right on dying until the siege was lifted and real milk was brought back.

By 1900 the scientists had learned a few things. They admitted there were two and possibly three diseases that could be cured by a change of diet. These were scurvy and beriberi, and possibly rickets. Some doctors claimed the rickets could be cured by the addition of certain things to the diet; others pooh-poohed the idea.

The cure for scurvy had come first. As far back as 1600 a few smart captains were giving their sailors oranges and lemons, and in 1753 an English captain, Lind, published a book telling of experiments made by him on English sailors. He declared scurvy could be cured by eating fresh fruits and vegetables or by the juice of citrus fruits. Fifty years later, a regulation was passed in the British Navy that all English sailors were to receive a small amount of lime juice every day.

A cure for the equally dread disease of beriberi, common in the Orient, was next discovered. A Japanese Navy doctor, Admiral Takaki, found that he could cure or prevent this deadly disease by feeding the sailors a more varied diet of vegetables, fish and meat, instead of their usually limited rations of white rice and dried fish. Also Dr. Eijkman, an army physician in Java, found he could cure his sick hens, and also his sick patients, by feeding them whole brown rice instead of milled white rice.

Rickets, the third disease, had long curved the leg bones and twisted the spines of many children, particularly in the poorer districts of northern Europe, England and America. Many doctors maintained that it could be cured by cod liver oil, but plenty of other leading physicians were still skeptical.

Still, in 1900 nobody knew *why* these foods would bring a cure. In fact, most doctors believed that all diseases were caused by germs, or else by something called *toxins* in the foods.

Experiments on animals were finally to break the germ-block in the scientists' minds and change the theories about nutrition.

Even before 1900 there had been a few pioneer animal experiments. Notable among these was the one by N. Lunin, a European scientist. He fed mice such mixtures as cane sugar, water and casein, a protein from milk. His uncooperative mice died in two to three weeks. Then there was Eijkman with his hens, and another Dutch scientist, Pekelharing, who baked bread out of milk casein, egg white, lard and white rice flour. His rats nibbled the bread eagerly at first, then in a few weeks lost their appetite and died. When they were also given some whey, the clear liquid from milk, they frisked around the cages in perfect health.

By 1906, thirteen papers had been published telling of experiments on animals with various diets. All these papers were buried in scientific journals, and most doctors were still satisfied with their germ theory as the cause of all diseases. Only a few had begun to have doubts.

In that year of 1906, one of the leading nutrition scientists in England, Dr. F. G. Hopkins, wrote a paper in which he said that men as well as animals had become adjusted to living on plant tissues or animal products over many thousand years. He said these foods must contain countless things besides the basic food elements. In scientific language he told his fellow scientists that they didn't know anything about the real contents of a good diet.

After these plain words the experiments on the little hungry animals continued, but there was little understanding of the reasons for their health or sickness. A couple of Norwegian scientists, Holst and Froelich, wanted to reproduce Eijkman's experiments on beriberi. Instead of using hens, they substituted guinea pigs. The little beasts remained healthy on a diet of cereal and cabbage. Then the scientists took away the cabbage, and put only cereal in the cages. Now, the scientist thought, the pigs will get beriberi just as Eijkman's hens did. Each day they looked eagerly into the small cages.

"Ya," they said. "Now they are looking sick."

A few more days went by. As they watched, they realized that something had gone wrong. The pigs were sick, all right, but they didn't have the muscle weakness and other symptoms of beriberi. They looked as if they had — yes they did have — another disease, scurvy.

"This is strange," they said.

They didn't realize this mistake was a notable step forward in vitamin research. It was the first experimentally produced scurvy in animals. Scientists were to find later that only monkeys, guinea pigs and man require vitamin C from plants. All other species can manufacture their own.

In the United States, chemists E. V. McCollum and Marguerite Davis were experimenting on rats. They fed them starch, sugar, salts, protein and butter, which they thought they had purified. These rats grew and prospered; but when lard or olive oil (not even purified) was substituted for the butter the rats sickened and died in a few weeks.

McCollum gradually realized that there was something in the butter that the rats must have to live. He tried a number of other purified fats. Some of them had this unknown something and others did not. He called this unknown *fat-soluble A*, because it was carried by fats. He found some of this fat-soluble A in the leaves of plants, too.

This was 1913. Scientists were now sure of two unknown substances required for the life of the little animals. One was the fat-soluble A. The other was the beriberi medicine, which McCollum called *water-soluble B*, because it was carried by water.

The year before, in 1912, a Polish chemist working in London on the beriberi-curing substance made a lucky guess about these unknowns — a guess that was to put his name in history. He said he thought that four diseases — beriberi, scurvy, rickets and pellagra — were all caused by a *lack* of some special something in the diet and not by germs at all. He called his special something *vitamines* because he thought they were related to certain chemicals, the *amines*, and because *vita* means life.

This paper by Casimir Funk was read widely by scientists, and many of them concluded that Funk was probably right. They were also impressed by the experiments which Funk told about. He had, he said, cured paralyzed and dying pigeons in a few minutes, with drops of the almost-pure beriberi vitamine which he had concentrated from a huge pile of rice polishings.

Gradually McCollum's fat-soluble substance came to be called vitamine A, and his water-soluble one, vitamine B. The spelling was changed later to *vitamin* because it was found the vitamins were not related to the amines.

For three decades after Funk gave them a name, these special substances, the vitamins, were to dominate the research and thinking of thousands of scientists. Not only four vitamins were found, but more than a dozen. A few of them could be manufactured in the digestive systems of certain animals. For humans, almost all had to be supplied in their food, either plant food or animal products such as meat, milk and eggs. If people were to stay healthy they must include in their diets some of the foods that supplied these vitamins.

Many scientists worked on the analysis of foods to see which ones supplied what kind of vitamins. Others tried to isolate the pure vitamins from the foods. Everybody knew by this time that the anti-beriberi vitamin was in rice polishings, the scrapings that were taken off the rice grain by the milling machinery. Getting the pure vitamin out of the polishings was another matter. Funk worked on it and secured his pigeon-curing liquid but never got the pure crystals. An American scientist, R. R. Williams, spent more than 20 years on this problem. Then he was beaten by two Danes who managed to secure a few of the precious white crystals first.

Getting these pure anti-beriberi crystals was a mammoth chemical job, since there was only one ounce of the crystals in 25 tons of rice polishings. Later, Williams was to be the first to synthesize, or make, the vitamin (B₁) from pure chemicals and reduce the price from $400 a gram to six cents.

In contrast to this huge task is the way in which the pure anti-pellagra vitamin was found. Pellagra, which killed hundreds every year in the Southern states, had been under study for many years. A public health doctor, Joseph Goldberger, had shown as early as 1915 that it was caused by too much corn bread and salt pork and not enough protective foods such as milk, meat and eggs. Many scientists had studied the disease, but 20 years later the anti-pellagra chemical had not been found.

Along with many others, a student at the University of Wisconsin, R. J. Madden, was experimenting on pellagra in dogs, called black-tongue. He thought he would try some of the vitaminlike chemicals that were around the laboratory. One day in 1937 he reached up on the shelf and pulled down a bottle and gave some of its contents to his sick dogs.

After a few days he was able to tell his teacher, Dr. Elvehjem, that the dogs were getting well. No more sore mouths or swollen tongues. The dogs which had been so sick were now hungry and playful.

Perhaps he shook the bottle of nicotinic acid crystals under the professor's nose and said, "Look, there's the anti-pellagra vitamin."

Vitamin C, the anti-scurvy vitamin, was also first secured while working on purely chemical problems rather than food hungers. Szent-Gyorgyi, a Hungarian chemist, isolated some crystals from adrenal glands, as well as cabbages and oranges, in 1928. He called it hexuronic acid. Later, scientist C. G. King of Pittsburg took some of the crystals and proved that this was indeed the true anti-scurvy vitamin. It was later called antiscorbutic acid.

Thus was finally solved the mystery of why 25 of Cartier's men died in the New World and why so many other sailors had died on

VITAMIN CRYSTALS —

Top left, vitamin A magnified; top right, vitamin B-1 magnified; bottom left, vitamin C magnified; bottom right, vitamin B-12 magnified

Smaller mouse shows vitamin B-12 deficiency.

the long sea voyages when all fresh foods were gone. Their dried concentrated rations did not have any vitamin C which their bodies had to have.

Fortunately for Cartier's men, the green needles of the hemlock tree furnished the needed vitamin and saved the lives of most of them. Somehow or other the Indians had found sometime in their past that the mashed cooked needles — probably only brought to a boil, since Indian cooking was done with hot rocks in baskets — would cure the sickness.

If Cartier's men had had a few ounces of the pure vitamin C crystals, such as Szent-Gyorgyi made, or a bottle of vitamin C tablets such as we can buy in any drug store today, none of the men need have died and all would have been spared much misery.

96

CHAPTER 10

SEEDS, FOODS AND FALLOUT SHELTERS

If you are an average young person, you probably live with your parents and one or more brothers and sisters. Do you know how much food it takes to keep this group of people for two weeks?

Perhaps you have gone with your mother to the supermarket on her weekly shopping trip. What did your mother buy?

She may have bought sugar and flour, rice and breakfast foods. Then she probably added a sack of potatoes and one of oranges, and maybe a bag of apples. She surely purchased quite a supply of meat, some fresh vegetables, such as carrots, lettuce and tomatoes, plus some canned ones, and perhaps some dried beans. Then she may have stopped at the frozen food bin and added some frozen vegetables as well as juices. She certainly bought a pound or two of butter or margarine. Then did she pick up some deserts such as packaged puddings, cake mixes or canned fruit? And what about milk products? If the milkman stops at your house she didn't put cartons of milk in her basket but she may have bought a piece of cheese, or a container of cottage cheese. Altogether the cart was piled high when she pushed it to the check stand.

When she unloaded the shopping bags at home on the kitchen

table the food made quite a pile, didn't it? Now multiply this by two and add some extras which were on the shelf at home. Can you picture this two weeks' food supply for your family?

However, suppose your mother were told that she must feed her family for two weeks on the food that she could store in a small cupboard, just two feet square. And she must use no refrigeration. She would certainly have to make some drastic changes in her shopping list.

First to go would be the foods that contain large quantities of water, because they are bulky and take up lots of room in storage. Things like tomatoes, apples, potatoes and the fresh and canned fruits. Cereals are dry, but many are packaged so loosely that they take up an enormous amount of space for the food energy they furnish, so they would not do. Meat and frozen foods would be out for two reasons, both because of bulk and because of lack of refrigeration.

What is left now in the shopping cart? The flour, sugar and dried beans are still there, and perhaps a box of rolled oats, or cream of wheat. They both furnish many food calories in comparison to their bulk. Perhaps there are dried peas and some cheese and dried meat.

Now your mother begins to plan meals such as many poor families over the world eat. These meals are made of breads of wheat or corn flour, boiled beans, cooked rice with an occasional piece of meat, cooked mush or farina, plus a few vegetables.

Then your mother is given further restrictions. She is told that she can't have enough heat to bake bread or cook beans or rice. She can have only enough to bring water to a boil. These last orders completely confuse your mother. She throws her hands into the air and shouts, "That's impossible. I give up."

Is it impossible? This is exactly the problem that was given to food experts by the government people who were planning fallout shelters which would offer protection in case of radiation attack. What could people be fed for two weeks, the government asked, that could be stored dry in a small space, could be prepared with little or no cooking, and at the same time would be tasty and acceptable.

Scientists at the Western Regional Research Laboratory at Albany, California, worked on this problem. Their first answer to the question was this:

"It would have to be some kind of a cereal product."

They said this because they were aware that for thousands of years the grains, or cereals, have been the mainstay of millions of people. Rice in the Orient, wheat in Europe and the Middle East, and corn in the Americas. Then too, the cereals furnish concentrated food, many calories for their bulk. And finally, they fill the last hard requirement, they can be kept for long periods without refrigeration, if they are dry.

Wheat, the scientists pointed out, is an excellent food — if the whole grain is eaten with only a little of the bran removed, but retaining the fat-and-protein-rich germ. The whole wheat grain contains starch, fats, minerals, small amounts of proteins and several vitamins, especially the B vitamins. Wheat, if kept dry, will continue to be edible for years.

To be a complete food, wheat would have to be fortified — or helped out — by extra protein, and a few vitamins, particularly vitamin C. However, the vitamins could be easily added, and the lack in protein would not be serious if people did not have to live too long in fallout shelters.

Wheat, then, was decided on, both because of its nutritive value, and because it's a food to which most American families are accustomed. However, in what form should this wheat be served? It had to be some wheat product that required little or no cooking.

This is when the word "bulgur" came into the planning.

"Why not some form of bulgur?" the experts asked each other.

A number of scientists at the Government's Regional Laboratory had been studying bulgur for some years. They had first become aware of it in Armenian dishes. Armenian restaurants often serve a dish known as *pilaf*. It is a tasty dish made of wheat and meat, and is prepared the way it has been made for centuries back in Armenia. Forms of bulgur or wheat for pilaf may also be found in some supermarkets. Pilaf is made out of wheat prepared in a certain way, and it has a delicious crunchy, nutty taste.

Inhabitants of the Middle East have been raising and eating wheat since the time of the first farmers. Scientists, such as Professor Braidwood, think the earliest farmers parched the wheat grains and then ground them. The ground wheat may have been eaten as mush, or perhaps made into flour and water cakes. Sometime later they learned to make bulgur, and perhaps even later, raised bread with yeast.

The people of the Middle East make bulgur by first boiling the wheat grains until they are tender, then spreading them in the sun to dry. Next, the wheat is sprinkled with water and rubbed in a mortar or sometimes just between the hands to remove the outer layers of bran. Then it is cracked with a stone or crude mill, after which it is stored in large earthenware jars. It will keep without spoiling in this form for a year or two. It is eaten in soups, or as stuffing in meat dishes.

Nutritionally, bulgur is an excellent food. It contains almost all the nutrients, or food elements, of the whole wheat grain.

"We'll make small cookies out of bulgur," the government scientists said.

Making bulgur in the laboratory

This they did. For flavor, and to keep the cookies from crumbling, they added some fat, and a little malt and salt.

A group of people in California volunteered to go into an air-raid shelter and see what it would be like to live there under conditions similar to that of a real air raid. There were 99 men, women and children in the group; 51 adults, 19 teen-agers and 29 children. They ate three meals a day. Each meal consisted of four bulgur cookies plus peanut butter or jam to spread on the dry cookies. Along with these they had either dehydrated milk or soup. For breakfast they ate two cookies crumbled into sweetened milk like cereal; the other two wafers were spread with jam. For lunch and dinner the two wafers were crumbled into soup, the other two were eaten with jam or peanut butter. There was instant coffee at each meal, and a small package of raisins for breakfast, and one of hard candy for dinner.

The test lasted two days and three nights. After it was over most of the people reported that they had had enough food to satisfy their hunger.

The foods which these people ate while they were in the shelter

People in a fallout shelter eating dinner of bulgur wheat, instant soup and jelly

came mostly from plants. In this respect they were not far different from meals which many people have been eating day after day all their lives, except for the precooking feature. Ordinarily, of course, most foods are cooked just before they are eaten, especially in primitive societies that do not have refrigeration.

It is always cheaper to eat plant products than to feed the plants to animals and then eat the animals, or their products such as milk, eggs or butter. Hence, the poor of every country eat more plant products than they do animal foods. The poorer the country, the larger proportion of people who go directly to the plants for their main food supply.

Scientists have found that the cells of plants are minute chemical factories in which several thousand different chemical steps or reactions take place. Some of these result in the production of vitamins, others in food materials such as proteins, fats and carbohydrates.

Energy for this manufacturing process comes from the sun. The plants can use this sun energy by means of their chlorophyll, the green coloring matter in leaves, as the Dutch physician Jan Ingenhousz proved. Raw products for this manufacturing are water and carbon dioxide, the bubbly gas in carbonated drinks. This gas, which can be made by burning carbon (such as coal or charcoal) with oxygen, is colorless and only slightly heavier than air. You can understand how much of it must be used by plants in their manufacturing when you realize that every day the plants of the world use up a weight of carbon equal to *forty million tons*.

The nutrients which are manufactured in the leaf cells are later moved to different parts of the plant where they are used for growth, or stored for later use or for the embryo when it starts to grow.

For a long time after the discovery of vitamins scientists thought that only animals and people required vitamins for life. They thought that plants somehow had them by accident, or perhaps as waste products in their growth processes, but didn't need them to live. However, they found by certain experiments when trying to grow separate parts of plants such as root tips in nutrient solutions (water containing plant foods), that plants are as dependent on vitamins as

102

are animals. The only difference is that the complete plants can manufacture their own vitamins.

As scientists found out more and more about this manufacturing process in the plant world, it became clear why people for many thousands of years have been able to secure much of their food from plants. Growing leaves have many vitamins that people need; seeds and roots have rich stores of certain vitamins as well as other nutrients. Of course, primitive people didn't know this. They only knew that the plants tasted good to them and helped them stay alive.

Seeds, especially, have been useful to man. A seed is made up of an undeveloped baby plant, the embryo, and a store of baby food to be used when the seed sprouts and the baby starts to grow. Around these, wrapping them securely to make a nice neat package, is a cover made of one or more seed coats.

Inside the fresh seed the food is a moist rich jelly. As the seed ripens, this jelly dries and hardens. This enables seeds to be stored a long time without spoiling.

These two properties of seeds, rich stores of food plus the ability to remain edible after long storage, have made them the main foodstuffs of the world.

By far the greater part of the food of all the people in the world consists of seeds, and most of these are the seeds of the grass family. Thus, the cereals such as corn, wheat, oats, rye and rice fill the world's foodbasket.

In spite of the number of people who eat corn, rye and oats, these grains are of lesser importance to the world population today, as a whole, than rice and wheat. Some scientists divide the world into what they call the *wheat world* and the *rice world*. In fact, they find that about four out of five of the earth's people belong to one of these worlds. As far back as history is written, rice has been the main food of the peoples of Asia, Japan and the Islands of Indonesia. Wheat has been the preferred food for Europeans, North Americans and many in other countries. For many of the people of the rice world their favorite food, rice, is three quarters of their total diet.

All cereal seeds are rich in starchy carbohydrates, with smaller amounts of proteins, minerals and vitamins. However, most of the minerals and vitamins are concentrated in either the embryo or the outer layers of the grains, which are not eaten when only white flour and white rice are served. This explains why modern eaters of these grains are apt to get vitamin deficiency diseases unless they eat enough foods that are rich in vitamins.

To produce either white flour or white rice, the outer layers of the seeds are removed. Modern milling machinery also removes the embryo (called the *germ* by millers). This makes white flour and white rice a good carbohydrate food and a moderately good protein food. It is poor as far as minerals and vitamins are concerned. As a result, beriberi still kills many people in Asia who like to eat white rice, but are too poor to buy vitamins or a variety of foods.

Much of the white bread sold in the United States is enriched, that is, it has had vitamins and minerals added to replace those which have been milled out. Dried milk is also added to many of the breads.

Legumes are the second great group of seeds that people use for food, and have used since ancient times. All kinds of beans, peas and lentils supply protein. Dry, they contain 25 to 40 percent protein and some are rich in carbohydrates as well. Some legumes, such as soybeans and peanuts, are high in oil and protein, as are certain other seeds, particularly rape, sesame and sunflower. Soybeans are 40 percent oil; peanuts are 50 percent. Seed oils furnished about 55 percent of the world's edible oils and fats in 1959.

The soybean is the most important leguminous seed in the world. In the United States we raise half of the world's crop, but process most of this for oil. In the Orient it has been an important seed food for hundreds of years.

In the United States only one-fourth of our foods comes directly from plants. The rest comes from animals which in turn are nourished on plants. In Europe one half of the food is plant food. In the Orient, about three quarters of the people's total food is seeds, roots or leaves.

Either way it's plants that feed the people of the world. All of us would soon starve without them, and life on our earth as we know it couldn't go on without green plants.

CHAPTER 11

GEORGE AND HIS RICE PROJECT

In March, 1953, George Gooneseng went to a meeting. It was sponsored by the United Nations and it seemed to George about the most important meeting that organization had ever held. In fact, George himself was on the platform in front of the microphone, and since George was only seventeen at the time, the whole thing was a big event.

The meeting was a result of an exciting thing that had happened in George's village the year before when an agricultural scientist from the United States had arrived. The agricultural man, Mr. Smith, had talked at George's school. He had come to Ceylon, he said, to organize the boys and girls of several villages into clubs such as were found in the United States.

"The young people in my country call their clubs the 4-H," Mr. Smith said.

He went on to say that the clubs in Ceylon would be open to any boy or girl of ten years or older who could have the use of one-eighth of an acre of land belonging to his father. On this land the new club member would grow rice.

"This rice must be grown a certain way," he told the boys and girls. "We are going to try out special things that have been found to give more and better rice in other countries." He smiled. "Maybe you can even beat your fathers at rice farming."

The boys and girls laughed politely at this little joke, but George clenched his fists tightly. He was almost a man, even if he was short and thin. Why couldn't he beat his father?

The rules for rice growing would include the use of steel plows, instead of the old-fashioned, wooden ones. The club members must thresh the grain with one of the new-type rotary threshers, where a man or boy pedals with his feet so that the grains of rice come out in a golden stream, instead of being trampled under the hooves of animals, which was the way threshing was generally done in Ceylon. The rice must be cut with a sickle instead of a small knife held in the palm of the left hand, as George's father did. All club members would be required to write in a recordbook everything they did to the rice.

Moreover, Mr. Smith said firms in the city of Colombo were going to give the new club members enough chemical fertilizer to enrich the soil and help the rice plants grow better.

The best thing of all Mr. Smith told at the end of his talk. When the harvest was in, he said, and the results had been judged, there would be prizes for the winners. The top winner of all would get a registered bull for his very own. Other prizes would be farm tools such as shiny new rakes and digging forks, and bags of improved rice seed for sowing the next year.

George ran all the way home from school that day. He could hardly breathe as he asked his father for permission to use a small corner of their precious land. Of course, George had helped his father ever since he was a small boy, pulling weeds and driving away the birds that came in large flocks each year, hoping to share in the harvest. But would his father trust him to cultivate a portion of their land all by himself as the club rules said he must?

His father looked grave when George asked him for some of the land, so that George almost lost hope.

"Will you work hard, son?" his father asked.

"Oh, I will, I will," George shouted. "You'll see."

"You mustn't run off to fly a kite when it is time to wade in the sticky mud and pull the weeds from among the young rice plants," his father warned.

George was insulted. "I am almost a man now. I am not interested in kites."

"Well. . ." his father said.

George knew this was permission. He ran out from the small grass-roofed house and danced for joy. In his mind's eye he could already see his new bull in the pen near the small barn. He could almost touch the bull's soft nose, and the silky hair along his neck. He could feel the puff of his warm breath as he blew on his new master's arm in pleasure when he was given a stalk of sugar cane.

The next day at school George signed up for the club program. He brought home a set of printed rules that he must follow. The first rule was that he must raise one-eighth acre of rice. This did not seem strange to George. What else could one do with a piece of land as important as raising rice?

George had lived all his life in Ceylon, which is part of what the experts call the rice world. This includes much of India and China, as well as Burma, Thailand, Japan and the Islands of Indonesia. It is also known as *Monsoon Asia*, because at certain times of year the strong winds, or monsoons, bring the rains that flood the rice fields. The island of Ceylon where George lives also has a hot climate. This is another reason why so much rice is raised there. Rice plants need warm weather to make them grow and ripen.

All his life George has seen his father, as well as all their neighbors, plant rice. Although their farms are very small in comparison with farms in the United States, these men raise enough for their families to eat and some extra to sell. After the rice is harvested other things may be planted for a second crop, such as beans, peanuts or sweet potatoes.

Every morning George has a bowl of rice for breakfast. He has rice for lunch and dinner, too, along with some vegetables and fruit, and perhaps a little fish. George doesn't get tired of eating rice. He thinks he's lucky to have rice to eat, because he knows there are poor people who cannot afford to eat rice this often. If you told George

Farmer sows rice in Ceylon.

that there are many people who eat bread made of wheat every meal even when they can afford rice, George would think this was very odd.

George was excited about the first meeting of the new club. He wore his best shirt and brushed his black hair until it shone. Mr. Smith talked a while and then asked the boys and girls to decide on the objectives for their club and choose an emblem. He read them some of the objectives that clubs in the United States had adopted and told them that the emblem for these clubs was a four-leaf clover.

The objectives of the club were adopted quickly. The boys and girls thought those suggested by Mr. Smith were fine. They were:

1) To learn more about growing rice and to have each member's field be a demonstration of good methods of rice growing.

2) To help Ceylon to be self-supporting in rice growing and to aid in the country's well-being.

3) To learn from club membership how to work with others, how to play with others, and how to conduct a meeting.

The choosing of the emblem turned out to be a real problem. No one wanted the clover leaf since that didn't mean much in Ceylon, but there the agreement ended. Everyone wanted something different. Finally, they took George's suggestion of an elephant with a rice bowl on its back.

108

"The elephant is highly valued in our country," George said. "He stands for dignity and strength. And the bowl of rice is what we are working for, plenty of food for all our people."

George worked hard on his project. First he dug up a small patch of ground near the house, then he made it nice and smooth with a hoe. This was the place to plant the special rice seed which the leader gave them. Next, he flooded the bed with water and scattered the rice seeds thickly, according to directions. When the tiny green shoots began to show through the water, George watched over them carefully. When they reached a certain size they would be ready to transplant.

While he was waiting, he hitched the family cow to the steel plow which the leader loaned him and plowed back and forth across the muddy field. The mud and water came up to his knees and it was hard to walk and even harder to hold the plow straight. When the plowing was finished he hitched the cow to a heavy wooden platform, like a door, and dragged this over the field to further soften and pulverize the lumps in the mud. George didn't mind this part of the work so much because he could ride on the drag instead of wading in the mud.

When the field was exactly right, and the young rice plants were strong and vigorous, George pulled up the plants and tied them in

Women transplant rice in Ceylon.

bundles. Then he waded across the field and pushed the young plants down into the soft oozy mud just the right number of inches apart. The plants looked droopy at first from such rough treatment, but the next day they were straight and fine-looking. George had a sore back from so much stooping, but when he saw the plants looking so fine in their neat rows, he didn't mind the aches in his back.

All season George watched over his rice. When the water was low in the field he opened the floodgates and let in more. When he saw weeds come up through the water and begin to take some of the precious sun and plant food away from his rice, he waded back and forth across the field, pulling out the weeds and stirring the mud around the roots of the rice plants. As the season progressed his rice plants stood thick and tall — more than four feet high if you counted the part of the stems under the water. They stood so close together that they looked like a green carpet that completely hid the water. When the wind blew, they swayed gently back and forth with a soft hissing sound.

Finally, George could see the heads of rice begin to come out from the tops of the leaf sheaths. The small green hulls didn't have any solid grains in them as yet, but George knew that many birds don't wait for the grains to get hard. They think the liquid "milk" that forms first is a wonderful treat.

George was determined that the birds shouldn't spoil a single head of his rice if he could help it. He strung wires across his plot and fixed bright pieces of tin on them. When he hit the wires with a stick the tin pieces jangled and made a noise that scared off the birds. George stayed out by his rice field so much of the time that his mother became worried.

"Son, you have to come into the house once in a while to eat and rest," she scolded him.

But George thought his rice was more important than food or rest. He grabbed a few handfuls of cold rice and dashed out to his precious field. When the rice was ripening, George also took his record-book out to the levee that enclosed the water, and worked on it while he watched for birds.

Finally, it was time to drain the water from the field. George could hardly wait then, for he knew he could harvest his rice soon. More than ever now he had to fight the birds. Flock after hungry flock came to his field and had to be driven away. Early morning and evening were the worst times, but no time was really safe. George's mother brought his rice and vegetables to the levee so he would eat.

"You look so thin, George," she scolded. "Let the birds have a mouthful and eat some yourself."

One day his father came out to the field. He pulled the grains from a couple of rice stalks and rubbed them in his hand. He looked at them critically and then he shelled a few grains with his teeth, and chewed the light brown kernels.

"It's ripe enough now," he said to George. "You can start cutting your rice tomorrow."

George jumped up and began to shout and dance. "Good, good, good," he said. "No more silly old birds. Tomorrow I put the rice away."

He looked at his field proudly. Since the water was not there to support the stalks they did not stand as straight and proud as before. The heavy heads leaned every which way. This did not worry George, because he knew that these heavy heads would yield many bags of golden grain.

The next morning George was the first one awake. His father scolded him fondly from his sleeping couch.

"Lie still a while, George," he said. "You can't start the harvest until the dew is gone."

George, however, was already out the door and on his way to his field, even though he could hardly see the path.

When the dew was finally gone, George began cutting his rice with a new kind of curved knife with a handle — a sickle — as specified in the club rules. Their club leader explained that this was one of the new methods the agricultural man, Mr. Smith, was introducing. He hoped it would help the Ceylon rice farmers to faster harvesting methods such as other countries used.

The new sickle seemed awkward at first, but George soon became used to it. He swung it with his right hand and gathered the cut stalks on his left arm. When he had a good-sized bundle he took some

Farmers prepare rice paddy fields in Ceylon.

of the straw and tied it together, then he put the bundles in a neat pile. It was hard work and the sun was very hot. The edges of the dried blades of rice scratched George's skin and the dust and chaff got into his nose and throat. If it hadn't been for the club record, and the prizes, George might have stopped awhile and rested.

All that day he worked, and the next. Finally, his rice was all cut. After the bundles were dry they had to be moved in a wheelbarrow to the barnyard and piled carefully in a big stack until he could get the use of the new threshing machine.

George looked proudly at his stack of rice. Was this a record crop for the size of his field? It looked fine to him, but he wasn't sure. He wished he had paid more attention to his father's rice farming in the past. Maybe then he would know better how to judge his crop. He looked at his father. What was the man thinking? Did he think this was a good crop, or only fair? George couldn't tell.

The club leader came around and arranged a time for George to use the new thresher. He looked critically at the big pile of rice but he didn't say a word about whether it was the biggest pile he had seen or not. George began to get worried. So many other boys were working for the prizes, too. And his heart was set on the beautiful bull.

When his turn came to use the thresher, George thought it looked a little like a sewing machine he had seen once on a trip to the city.

You sat in front of it and pedaled with your feet, while you stuffed the rice heads into the top. The machine had a rotor inside with spikes which tore the grains from the straw, so that the rice fell down on a mat in a golden pile. His father came to watch him use it.

"See, Father," George said. "It's much better than beating the rice with sticks or driving the silly old cows around over it. They always break so much of the grain." And he added, "It doesn't have to be shaken in the baskets either, to get rid of the straw. Mother should be pleased about that."

His father smiled. "The young are always anxious to try new things," he said.

After the rice was threshed it had to be dried. To do this George spread it out in a thin layer in the sun, just as his father did. Of course, the birds wanted some of this fine golden food. George had to keep shooing them away with a fan on a long pole.

Eventually, the rice was safe in bags, and stored in the small grass-roofed rice shed by the barn. Everything was done now except writing the last entries in the recordbook. And getting his exhibit ready, and his talk. That talk! George shuddered.

"Why choose me?" he had asked the club leader when he had told George he had been picked as the one member from their club to give a talk. "One of the other boys could do it better," George said. "I'll arrange the exhibits."

But the club leader had been firm. One member from each club had to give a talk, he had said, telling what he had learned of the new rice farming methods. He had added, "I think you can give a fine talk."

If it hadn't been for the dread of the talk the final day, the meeting would have been pure joy to George. It was held in the city of Colombo, a place where George had been only once. Just the trip alone would have been a thrill.

George sat numbly in the chair. His rice had been examined and weighed. His recordbook, which the leader had said was very neat, had gone into the exhibit. Some of his golden rice, too, was there for everyone to see. But that talk! It was a nightmare. There was a big crowd in the meeting hall. Besides all the club members there were parents and officials from the villages.

The boys who were to give the talks were ushered onto the stage, along with the club leaders and Mr. Smith. Toward the front of the stage there was a microphone. George had been told that he had to talk into that thing. He sweated as he waited his turn. Even though he had written his speech and had practiced and practiced out in the barnyard, he knew he wouldn't be able to say a word.

About halfway through the meeting Mr. Smith motioned to George and introduced him. Somehow or other George got over to the microphone and leaned toward it. As he began to talk a strange thing happened. He forgot about the crowd out in front and how scared he had been. He thought only of the beautiful rice as it had shone golden in the sun. He thought of it as it had moved in the wind, like waves in water, with a whispering that promised a bountiful harvest. Never mind about the beautiful bull which some other boy would have. He, George, had brought in the golden sheaves of rice and threshed them as his father had done, and his father's father — food for the people of Ceylon. Only he had learned new things, too — new ways that would give more and better harvests, so that none should go hungry.

As George sat down he was surprised to hear that there was a great clapping of hands. He sat in his chair limp and exhausted, only half listening to the other contestants.

114

Suddenly he heard his name called and realized that the other club members on the stage were motioning to him.

"George Gooneseng," Mr. Smith said. "Please step forward."

George went to the center of the platform. The rest was almost like a dream, but later George found it was true.

"It gives me great pleasure," Mr. Smith said, "to award you the first prize in the rice growing contest. Not only did you make a fine talk here today, but you raised 76 bushels of paddy [unhulled] rice per acre — a yield of 22 more bushels than your father raised on the same kind of land. Here is a certificate for the prize bull. He will be waiting for you to take him home."

CHAPTER 12

ROOTS FOR BREAD—MANIOC, TARO AND POTATOES

Although four out of five of the world's people belong to either the wheat world or the rice world, there are other large groups of people who have a different staff of life. Many of these have seldom, if ever, seen a piece of wheat bread or a dish of rice. They live in parts of the world where wheat and rice do not grow well, and are expensive. The food which they eat day after day, as we eat bread, comes from a tuber, the root of the manioc plant. In English-speaking countries this plant is called cassava.

If you were to visit Ghana in West Africa, you might meet Kudjo who lives in a small village at the edge of the forest. It's always hot in Ghana so Kudjo doesn't have to worry much about clothes. When he was little he went naked, but now that he is older he wears a pair of shorts when he's at home. For school he adds a shirt. Sometimes when he wants to dress up he wraps a colorful cotton robe around his body and throws the end of the robe over his left shoulder. This covers his right arm but leaves his left arm free.

Kudjo's house, like all the rest in the village, is made of mud, which is nicely smoothed and hardened so it looks like brown stucco. Kudjo thinks his house is quite modern because it has a corrugated iron roof. His grandfather always lived in a house with a thick grass roof.

"The iron roof never leaks, even when it rains hard," Kudjo says proudly.

Kudjo's home is shaded with palm trees. The dirt of the yard is dry and hard-packed. One side of the yard is covered with red peppers and purplish-brown cocoa beans laid out to dry. Kudjo helped his father gather the pods full of cocoa beans from the white-barked cacao trees which grow in the forest. Then he helped him break open the pods and spread the beans out to dry in the hot, sunny yard. When they are dry his father will sell them and get money, about the only money the family sees. For a sixty-pound load of cocoa beans his father will receive about nine dollars.

Kudjo also helps his father get the land ready to farm. First they have to cut down the trees and brush. Once, long before Kudjo was born, this land had big mahogany and kapok trees growing on it. These were cut down and crops were planted for three years. At the end of that time the land was thought to be worn out because things didn't grow very well in it any more, so it was abandoned. Right away, the wild plants began scattering their seeds in the neglected farm and soon it was a green jungle once more. Now Kudjo's father says he thinks it will be fertile again so they will use it.

After the trees and brush are cut down and allowed to dry, there comes a day which Kudjo likes very much. It is the day of the big fire. His father starts a fire at one end of the field, and the flames roar and crackle as they race along. Not only is it very exciting to see the fire but also it usually brings them good things to put in the stew pot. As the fires roar across the field small animals such as rats, snakes and lizards are driven from their homes. Kudjo and his father stand at the lower end of the field with clubs, and usually manage to kill several. However, they have to be very careful because some of the snakes are poisonous.

After the fire is burned out and the ground is cool enough to walk on, Kudjo's mother comes to plant the first crop. Since this is women's work, his father doesn't help, but sometimes Kudjo comes along with his mother. The field is a long walk from the village. Kudjo's baby sister goes, too. She rides all the way on her mother's back. She is tied on snugly with a bright print scarf, so that Kudjo can

Mother crushes cassava in street, baby on her back.

see only her head and tiny feet sticking out from the scarf. Long before they reach the field she is sound asleep, as if she had been rocked in a cradle.

The first crop on this new ground will be corn. This is planted by digging a hole through the ashes which are still on the ground, and dropping in three or four grains, then covering them with dirt. Kudjo thinks it's fun to push the dirt over the corn grains with his bare toes.

As soon as the rains come the corn sprouts and grows quickly. Since there are two growing seasons in one year in this hot climate, there will be a second crop of corn in this same field.

The next year his mother will plant cassava. Instead of dropping seeds she will cut the stems from some of the cassava plants which were grown in another field the previous year. Each section of stem must have a bud on it so the new plant can start from this bud. The pieces of stem, about a foot long, are laid in a hole or shallow trench in the ground and covered with dirt.

The cassava plants grow very fast. They have big leaves like some of our ornamental plants. Each leaf has five to seven divisions fastened together at the center to make a spreading green fan. Soon the field looks like a small jungle with the trees about six to twelve feet high. This jungle is allowed to grow for a year or more before the roots are big enough to eat. Often Kudjo's mother plants other things that ripen sooner, such as yams or beans, in between the cassava plants.

118

When the roots are big enough to eat, Kudjo goes with his mother to dig some for their dinner. Not all the crop is harvested at once, because the roots keep better in the ground than they do in the house. Although Kudjo thinks his home is quite modern, there is no refrigeration of any kind in his house. In fact, there is none in any house in the village. Since the weather is hot and often wet, most foods spoil quickly, except dry ones like corn. Some foods are dried over a fire to preserve them.

Kudjo helps his mother carry home the roots. He lets her carry the bigger ones, because sometimes there are one or two that weigh as much as twenty pounds. Most of them, however, are about two feet long and quite slender.

Kudjo and his family are all hungry when he and his mother and the baby get home from the field with the cassava roots. Kudjo runs out to the well and brings a bucket of water for his mother so she can wash the roots. Then she peels and slices them and puts them in a pot with some water. Kudjo starts a charcoal fire in a small iron stove not much bigger than the pot, and his mother sets the cassava on to cook.

Manioc plantation

"Watch the baby so she doesn't crawl too near the fire," his mother warns.

It seems to Kudjo as if the pot will never boil. When the slices of cassava are finally soft, his mother takes them off the fire. She puts them into a wooden container, like a bucket without handles.

"Bring me the masher," she says to Kudjo.

He hands her a smooth clean stick almost as big as a baseball bat. With this she mashes the pieces of cassava into a sticky paste and adds a generous amount of orange-colored palm oil. Then she calls the family.

"Come and eat," she says. "The *fu-fu* is ready."

Sometimes his mother puts some bananalike plantains on to fry over the small fire after she has cooked the cassava. Or, the family may have peanuts to eat with their fu-fu, as well as bananas or other fruit for dessert. Sometimes there is a little meat, most often fish. The family likes this very much but cannot always afford to have it. Once in a great while they have chicken, which makes Kudjo very happy, for this is a great treat.

Cassava, or manioc, didn't come originally from Kudjo's country, or even from any part of Africa. Like corn, it's an ancient plant that has been so long with people that the wild ancestor has been lost. Scientists think it came originally from South America, somewhere in the Amazon basin of Brazil. There are many varieties of manioc known now, and most of them contain a poison, so that anyone eating a root raw would die or at least become very ill.

It's hard to understand how primitive hunter-gatherer men discovered that if this poison were squeezed out the root would be good to eat. However, long, long ago some bright person did find it out somehow, and taught others.

Some tribes of South American Indians have a clever system of removing the poison. First they weave a long tube of fibers from a palm tree. This tube, some five to eight feet long and about six inches wide, is open at the top and closed at the bottom. The manioc roots are peeled and then grated on a board which has stones fastened onto it with pitch. The stones are hard and have been broken so that they have sharp edges. One explorer told of finding a raw diamond fastened to a manioc grating board in one of the Guianas.

After grating, the shredded manioc is put into the tube which is compressed by a weight fastened to the bottom. This stretches the tube and gives it a smaller diameter, which presses out the juice. Often a pole is fastened to the bottom of the tube and one or two women sit on the pole. Their weight compresses the tube and squeezes out the juice.

Portuguese adventurers carried the stems and roots of the manioc plant from South America to Africa in the early days of exploration of these continents. Later it was taken to the South Seas, to Java, India and Indonesia. It has been and still is the basic food of many millions of people in the tropics of South and Central America, as well as southern Mexico. It is the bread of other millions in western Africa, as well as many of the poorer people in India, Ceylon, Java and other islands of Indonesia and the Pacific. These people would prefer rice, but they are too poor to buy it, and the land which they farm is too worn out or too eroded to raise it. Poor people in the Philippines make a substitute rice by whirling the shredded and sieved pulp of the manioc root in a rice winnowing basket. They keep on shaking the basket with a circular motion until small pellets about the size of rice are formed.

Manioc or cassava is a warm-weather plant that won't grow where there is any frost. It thrives best where the ground is rich and fertile, but it will grow better than most crops even when the soil is poor and no fertilizer is added. Also, it will stand a long dry spell of weather better than most food plants.

In fact, more food per acre can be raised with this plant than with any other crop. Yields run up to 20 tons per acre, as much as two or three times the amount that can be produced with other food plants.

Another great advantage of this crop for the tropics is that the roots may be left in the ground until needed, as Kudjo and his family do. This is important in hot countries where there is little or no refrigeration. Dry flour, as well as the coarser *farina* and tapioca which can be made from manioc roots, can also be kept easily without spoiling.

In spite of these advantages, the manioc plant is a poor food, and people who eat it are often undernourished. Imagine yourself, eating tapioca day after day — not tapioca pudding made rich and tasty with eggs, milk and sugar, but just plain tapioca, boiled and perhaps seasoned with peppers and onion.

Nutritionally, manioc is a much poorer food than wheat or rice or any of the grains. The root consists mainly of fiber and starch with almost no protein, fats, minerals or vitamins. Remember, it's different from the seeds or grains in which the plant has stored rich baby food for the new plant. Instead, the root acts only as a storage reservoir of starch which can be changed by the plant to sugar when it needs additional energy.

Many of the peoples who eat manioc regularly are too poor to buy the additional foods, particularly proteins, which would give them a well-balanced diet. For instance, in some districts of Java, in Indonesia, the poor people can afford to eat only once a day. Their whole meal may consist of a plateful of steamed cassava roots, a small onion and some chili pepper for seasoning. This food costs them about a penny per person per day. Some are even too poor for this, and eat only once in two days. Among these people there is

Left, woman prepares daily bowl of cassava. Right, utensils used in preparing cassava. Cassava roots at right are peeled (center foreground), grated on tin grater (left), partly dried by hand in basket (right background), then by pressure in smaller bowl (extreme left). Flour is sifted through handmade sieve (center) and slightly roasted as shown in background.

 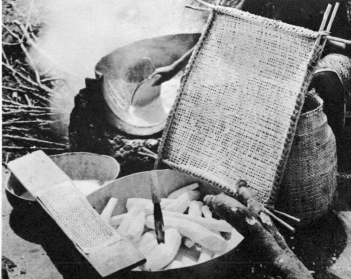

much disease due to malnutrition, particularly among the young children. After they are weaned, and can no longer drink their mother's milk, many develop a serious disease known as *kwashiorkor*. This is caused mainly by a lack of protein foods such as milk, eggs and meat. Even half a cup of milk a day would prevent this disease in many of these children.

The poverty of these people is not due to laziness, but rather to overcrowding of the country and the fact that there is so little industry that there is little income except from farming. More than 70 percent of the people of Indonesia are farmers, and 55 million of them live on the island of Java. Most of the farmers own or farm less than one acre of land, and some of that is hill land and rocky or badly washed by the tropical storms.

Conditions in many parts of tropical South America are not much better. For example, in northern and eastern Brazil, farina is the staple food and is sacked and sold as flour is in our country. It's the cheapest and often the only food for many of the people except for whatever wild game they are able to capture.

Farina is often manufactured in primitive mills in which a horse or ox walks in a circle, hitched to a beam. This moving beam operates a series of wooden gears that turn a wooden roller at high speed. The roller is covered with sharp spikes, which shred the peeled and washed manioc roots when they are pushed against it. The wet mushy mass is put through a sieve to remove the coarse fibers. Then it is carried to a crude press. This press is like a box with a movable top which slides up and down inside. The top of the box is forced down by the weight of heavy rocks or by a big wooden screw turned by manpower. After the plant juices, including the poison, are pressed out, the shredded material is spread on sheets of tin over a fire and stirred until it is dry. The resulting farina is about as coarse as our cornmeal.

Farina is eaten dry, or if the family is lucky enough to have a small piece of meat, the farina is mixed with the gravy from the meat, often with onion seasoning. Other slightly more prosperous South American people eat cooked manioc roots together with beans, rice

123

or corn. These are usually the sweeter varieties of the root, in which there is less poison so that it is safe to eat them after boiling.

Manioc flour is made in much the same way as farina, except the roots are ground to a finer pulp and the starch (or flour) is washed out with water. The flour is allowed to settle out of the water in big settling tanks, and then dried and shoveled into bags. The products of manioc, both farina and flour, are the chief food of the laborers of Brazil. The flour is also exported to the United States and Europe. It has many uses including glue, thickening for food products, and the production of tapioca. To make tapioca the manioc starch is heated and at the same time stirred.

Most of the manioc flour for export, as well as much of that eaten at home, is now made in factories. In Brazil there are large manioc plantations and factories with modern machinery to process the crop.

There are other root crops that are the bread, the main food, of large groups of people. In many of the South Pacific islands, the staple food is the mashed root of the taro plant. This is a tropical plant with big elephant-ear leaves and a bulbous root that grows in marshy land. The root is cooked and mashed. Then water is added to make a kind of sticky mush.

The Hawaiians call this *poi*, and they are very fond of it. Formerly it was mashed on big, hand-carved boards with stone poi-pounders. In old-time Hawaii it was eaten by dipping the fingers into a common bowl, and then putting them into the mouth. Thick poi was known as one-finger poi, and thinner kinds as two-finger or three-finger. Today, poi also is made in modern factories.

The people of the Pacific islands never depended on this starch food alone. They had other foods, such as bananas, sweet potatoes, coconuts, pigs and a variety of seafoods.

Another root crop that is now a common food in both Europe and the United States wasn't found in either of these countries before Columbus landed in America.

When the Spanish conquerors who followed Columbus reached the highlands of Peru they found the Indians eating a certain kind of round white tuber not much bigger than a walnut. The Spaniards tasted some and found that they were very good. Indeed, they liked them so well that they took a few back to Spain and planted them. This was the introduction of white potatoes to Europe.

To the Indians of the Andes, the potato was a staple food which their ancestors had been eating for untold generations. This was true particularly in the parts of the country that were too high to grow corn. Like corn, the potato has been so long with man that its wild ancestor has been lost.

In order to have a staple food which would keep through the long cold winter these Indians invented a food they call *chuño*. To make this they spread potatoes on the ground and let them freeze during the night. The next day the men, women and children mash them with their feet. That night the potatoes freeze again, and the next day they are again trampled. After four or five days of this treatment most of the water is gone from the potatoes. They will

Cassava on sale at market in Leopoldville, the Congo

keep throughout the winter. This is a primitive method of making dehydrated potatoes.

After the potato reached Spain it spread to other countries. In Ireland, in particular, it found a good home. Indeed, the potato became such a popular food in that country that it is known as the Irish potato.

Potatoes, like other starchy tubers and roots, are a good food if they are eaten along with other things. The potato is somewhat better than manioc, since the potato has a little more protein and a fairly good content of vitamin C. However, much of this vitamin is lost if potatoes are stored for several months.

All people, as scientists found out by feeding their little animals, need a certain amount of the basics plus vitamins and minerals. The grain foods and the root foods *by themselves* are all lacking in one or more of these. They must be eaten along with other foods to make a complete diet.

CHAPTER 13

TOOLS FOR EARLY FARMERS

Early farmers did not leave written records of the tools they used. Science detectives — the anthropologists — have to dig out the facts by studying one clue after another.

Some of the clues come from mounds like Jarmo. There were the pieces of sharpened stone that fitted together to make a curve. Remember? They had pitch on the dull side as if they had been fastened in a wooden handle to make a sickle, or reaping tool. Also the sharpened edges had the shine of some kind of grass-cutting on them.

There is a good deal of arguing among scientists as to whether a sickle shine actually means farming, or only an advanced kind of gathering. Some say the sickle could have been used to cut grass, or *wild* grain.

Others say, "No. Wild grains such as wild wheats would not have been collected with a sickle." Wild grasses, they point out, have brittle stems that allow them to scatter their seeds. Such seeds have to be collected by being brushed into a gathering basket. If they are cut with a sickle too much of the grain falls to the ground and is lost. Therefore, a sickle with shine on its edge means *cultivated* grain that has lived with man long enough to lose some of its brittleness.

Other clues about the tools of early farmers come from studying the things used today by primitive people. The most universal tool of all is the digging stick.

According to our modern way of thinking the digging stick is not much of a tool. It is simply a stout, straight stick about three to five feet long with one end sharpened to a point. Usually this point has been hardened by fire. This is done by heating the stick over coals, at the same time being careful that the stick doesn't catch fire.

The digging stick came long before farming. It is found among hunter-gatherer peoples in all parts of the world. It's the tool of the women who dig roots and bulbs. In Australia where there are still a few wandering tribes who have almost no possessions, the women have digging sticks to dig roots. They also use them to kill small animals such as snakes and rats.

In southwestern Africa a few Bushmen still live much the same kind of life except that they have some clothing made of skins. A writer who lived near a camp of Bushmen for some time told of going on a foraging expedition with a small elderly Bushman woman. With her pointed digging stick this little old woman dug a hole in hard-packed dry ground more than three feet deep and two feet across. She was trying to get a big root which she wanted for food. She couldn't pull it out, however, and had to give up. A short time later she found another root and made another large hole. This time she secured the root.

Scientists feel certain that the digging stick was carried over into the first agriculture and became one of the first farming tools. They have collected evidence by studying primitive farmers today in isolated parts of the world.

In southern Mexico near the border of Guatamala, there are a few Indians known as Lacadones. Remnants of the once mighty Mayas, these Indians are primitive farmers. Their only farming tools are the digging stick and the machete, or big knife. In January the Lacadone farmer cuts down trees and brush with his machete. As soon as the wood is dry he burns as much of it as he can. In May he sharpens

Ethiopian farmer uses digging stick.

one end of a stout stick with the machete to make his planting tool. With this stick he pokes a hole through the ashes into the ground and drops a few grains of corn into the hole. There are still stumps and half-burned logs in his field, but these are too big to bother with. The farmer plants his crop in the ground between and around them.

Besides corn, this Lacadone farmer raises beans, sweet potatoes, chili, onions, garlic and calabash gourds, as well as tobacco. He also has bananas, pineapples, papayas, lemons and other fruits. Besides these he gathers wild fruits and honey. All digging and planting is done with the digging stick. Fire and the machete are the only other tools. There are no hoes and no plows.

Traders sometimes reach this isolated area. The Lacadones sell tobacco and handmade bows and arrows to the traders. In return they get machetes, cheap liquor and sometimes — the greatest treasure of all — a shotgun. Meat comes from chickens they raise and game they kill in the forest.

Two or three years after he has cleared his land, the Lacadone farmer sees that his corn is not as good as it was. Also weeds have come in to share the ground with his crops and crowd them. Now he knows it's time to clear another plot of ground and start a new farming place.

129

The Lacadones are not the only people who still use the digging stick. In the Amazon basin of Brazil, there are tribes that plant dryland rice using the same tools, fire and the pointed digging stick. Many other primitive farmers still use this ancient stick.

Sometimes a circular stone with a hole in the center is threaded on the stick. This weights the stick and makes it easier to use in hard ground.

Dr. Robert Heizer of the University of California was interested in finding out about the ancient people whose trash piles were found in a cave near La Venta, Mexico. He decided he would study the people who were living today in this same vicinity. On the island of La Venta, he found Don Sebastian Torres and his family.

Don Sebastian is ninety-four years old. With him on the island are his sons and sons-in-law, their wives, their children and grandchildren.

"It is a fine place to live," Don Sebastian says. "I have been here since I was a young man."

The first modern inhabitants of the island were four young men. Among them was Don Sebastian's father-in-law. There were many wild animals on the island in those days. It was the favorite hunting ground of people in the surrounding area. There was no one left of the former ancients that had lived there, the ones who had built the stone monuments so interesting to scientists today.

The four young men decided they would settle there. They cleared the land as they had been taught by their fathers. It was hard work but they had strong arms and their machetes. Two wanted to raise cattle, one hogs, and the other planted coffee trees. Naturally, all of them planted corn, for that is the bread of their people.

Don Sebastian came to La Venta in his twenties. He is still there raising a few cattle and pigs, some coffee and, of course, corn. Although he lives fairly close to a town and is far more civilized than the Lacadone Indians, he uses almost the same tools for farming. He still raises his corn as his ancestors did before him.

This method of raising corn is simple to tell about, but it takes much hard work. It is a system of planting the ground for one year and letting it lie fallow, or rest, for four. Each year a place for the corn must be cleared. The brush and small trees are hacked down with machetes, allowed to dry and then burned. Since they have been growing only four years, the trees will not be big.

In May or early June the corn is planted. Holes three or four inches deep are made with a hardwood digging stick. Five grains of corn are dropped into each hole. Don Sebastian doesn't have a plow. The only other agricultural tool he uses is a *coa*, which is like a small curved·spade.

In December Don Sebastian chops down the cornstalks and weeds in his summer cornfield and plants a second crop. This one won't be as good as the first but in the warm climate of Mexico it will mature and furnish some corn. The next year the field will start its resting time again, and the wild plants will take over.

In some parts of the world the digging stick long ago gave way to the hoe and the spade. Also long ago, in some place, the plow was invented. Dr. Braidwood says that as far back as six thousand years ago the descendants of the first farmers at Jarmo were using primitive plows to get the soil ready for planting. They were still living in that part of the world where their great-great-great-grandfathers had lived. They were still raising wheat and other grains. Plow agriculture probably means that they had tamed animals to pull the plow.

After plowing, came the planting. This was done by a man (or perhaps a woman) wearing a sack of grain over one shoulder. As he walked he reached into the bag for handfuls of grain and scattered them on the plowed ground.

After the grains had been sprinkled on the whole field they were probably covered with dirt. In early days this was often done by cutting down a small tree and dragging it back and forth across the field. Or the grain was covered by hitching an ox to a drag made of logs or heavy boards. The dirt pushed over the grains of wheat not only made it sprout better, but protected it from hungry birds.

"Man must have been a food-gatherer a half million years before he invented farming," Dr. Braidwood says. Therefore, he points out, the development of the plow in approximately another three thousand years was truly remarkable.

The first plows were very crude. They were hardly more than

Drawing, based on ancient Egyptian reliefs, shows plow culture as compared with older and slower hoe culture.

heavy digging sticks set at an angle so they would scratch the soil as they were pulled along. A beam crossed the plowing stick at an angle so an ox could be hitched to it. One or two handles slanted off in the other direction so a man could hold on and guide the plow. Some plows took three men to operate. One man leaned on the plow and pushed the point into the ground, the second held the plow handles, and a third drove the oxen. Even this was better and faster than hacking at the soil with the digging stick or the crude hoes.

The plow made it possible to produce more food with fewer men working. This left other men free to do other kinds of work besides raising food. The plow made an enormous contribution to the great civilization of Egypt. It enabled the farmers to feed city dwellers as well as themselves. Early Egyptian paintings show plows being pulled by two oxen.

Agriculture didn't develop the same way or at the same speed in different parts of the world. Just as some peoples are still using digging sticks today, so some people advanced from digging stick to hoe agriculture and no farther. North and South American Indians never developed the plow. Perhaps this was because there were no horses or cattle they could tame.

132

Many of the American Indian tribes used the digging stick for planting, but they also had hoes for softening the ground to get it ready for planting. Some of these hoes were single tree limbs shaped like a capital L. Others had wooden handles and hoe blades of the shoulder bone of a deer or buffalo. Some had blades of stone or shell fastened to a stick with a bend near the end.

Usually digging stick and hoe agriculture was woman-power agriculture. The men's part of the work was to get the land ready for planting by cutting and burning. When plows were developed this usually meant that men would do the hard work of plowing.

The sickle for reaping wheat and other small grains began as a stone-edged tool and then as the centuries passed was given a bronze, and finally an iron, blade. The hoe was given a metal blade, too. Sometimes even the digging stick was iron-pointed. The plow, too, was fitted with an iron point and then a whole iron blade, called a *plowshare*.

Here agriculture remained, until something exciting began to happen in northern Europe and the United States. This something was to bring about the *second agricultural revolution* — which would allow farmers to produce food in more abundance than the world had ever dreamed possible.

CHAPTER 14

MEN, HORSES AND THRESHING MACHINES

Farmers in the early part of the nineteenth century, even in the United States and Europe, were still using essentially primitive tools. The cutting edges were not made of stone, because metal had long ago replaced it. But the design of many of the tools and the kind of tools used were practically the same. Horses were doing part of the work for the farmer. They pulled wagons and plows, but most of the hard work of a farm was still done by the muscles of men and women.

Joe Armour, as well as his sister and three brothers, knew all about the hard work on the farm. In 1858, five years before the beginning of the Civil War, Joe was eleven years old. He was the next to the youngest brother and his sister was a year older than he. They lived on a 200-acre farm in Indiana, 15 miles from the nearest town. Since the only way to go to town was in the farm wagon or on horseback, Joe saw the town only two or three times a year. This didn't matter, however, for the family raised nearly everything they needed.

Flour for their bread and cakes came from their own wheat, which they took to the mill to be ground. The root cellar was full of potatoes, apples and vegetables such as squash, turnips and cabbage. The meat house was hung with smoked ham, shoulders and sides of bacon. There was a barrel of maple sugar in the pantry made from the sap of their own maple trees. Sitting beside the barrel were crocks of cooked sausage preserved with a covering of white lard.

The cycle of planting began in the fall when the winter wheat was sown. First the soil had to be plowed. The team of brown horses with white nose patches, Daisy and Frank, were hitched to the plow. As they patiently walked back and forth across the field, the fresh brown earth was turned up behind the plow in a furrow a foot wide. Both of Joe's older brothers were good farmers and could guide the plow so that the furrow was as straight as if it had followed a line run by a surveyor.

After the field was plowed it had to be smoothed. This was done by hitching the team to a harrow and dragging it back and forth across the field. The harrow had been made by Joe's father. It was four heavy boards fastened together. Pounded through the boards were iron spikes which stuck down into the ground. It was Joe's task to do the harrowing.

To Joe, the harrowing was one of the pleasantest tasks of the year. In the crisp cool mornings of early fall he would go out to the barn and put the leather harness on Frank and Daisy. Then, riding Daisy and leading Frank, he would go out to the field, slide off and hitch the horses to the harrow. As he walked slowly across the field he had plenty of time to look at the sugar maple trees on the hill, flaming red and yellow in their fall colors. Or he could watch the flock of blackbirds which often followed the harrow, to pick up the worms and bugs that were uncovered. Also Joe enjoyed this time of year because it was an extra vacation from school. Joe knew that none of the older boys would be allowed to start school until the winter wheat was planted and the corn harvested.

As soon as Joe had smoothed one side of the field, one of his brothers would start planting wheat. Joe's father believed in keeping up with modern methods of farming, so instead of sowing the wheat by hand they now had a machine. To be sure it was worked by hand but it was a great improvement over the old method of reaching into a sack for handful after handful of grain to scatter. The machine was carried by a strap across one shoulder. It had a bag for the wheat which sifted down on top of a small fan. When the sower turned a crank the revolving fan threw the wheat out more than ten feet in a continuous spray.

"With this gadget, a child could plant an even field," Joe's father maintained.

"Well, why don't you let me plant then?" Joe asked eagerly.

All his father said was, "You stick to your harrowing, son."

There was plenty of this to do because the harrow had to be dragged over the whole field again after the wheat was dropped. This second harrowing covered the grain with soil.

As soon as the wheat was planted it was time to begin harvesting the corn. To do this they fastened high boards to one side of the farm wagon. Then they hitched the team to the wagon and slowly moved back and forth across the cornfield. The men walked on the open side of the wagon and grabbed the ears of corn from the stalks. They removed the husks with the help of a small iron gadget which they fastened to their right hands. The husker looked something like a modern beer can opener strapped to the hand with leather. As they walked they grabbed the ears of corn, tore off the husks and threw the ears into the wagon.

Joe was a good husker and could almost keep up with his older brothers, who always worked as if they were racing each other. Bang, bang went the ears of corn against the high side boards of the wagon as Frank and Daisy pulled it along.

The loads of corn were stored in corncribs, where the ears gleamed yellow through the cracks between the boards. The pumpkins, too, were hauled in from the field, and put in a golden pile in one side of the granary.

Now the time had finally come for school, and there were no more excuses. Joe's sister and his younger brother had started several weeks before. Now Joe and his two older brothers joined them each morning to walk the two miles to school. Before they could start in the morning they had to do the chores. All the stock, the horses, cows, sheep, pigs and chickens, had to be fed and watered. Also the stalls of the horses had to be cleaned for the day, and fresh straw spread underfoot.

Joe was always glad when spring came. He liked to see the ice leave the creek, and he always watched eagerly for the first new green grass. The two older boys stopped school as soon as the frost had left the ground and it was dry enough to plow. They had many days of plowing to get ready for corn planting. Also there were oats to plant so the horses could have grain to eat.

School soon ended for the year and then it was time for corn planting. Everybody watched the buds on the hickory trees. They knew when the buds were as big as squirrels' ears, it was time to start planting.

Corn planting was tiresome, Joe admitted to himself. But he was so glad to have school over that he didn't really mind. It was pleasant to be out in the fields again, and the plowed earth felt soft under his feet.

To plant corn, Joe first made a shallow hole in the earth with his hoe. Then he took a handful of shelled corn from a bag he wore over his shoulder. Dropping four or five grains into the hole, he covered them with soil with the hoe, took two steps, then made another hole. Joe tried to keep the holes the same distance apart and in a straight line. Looking back he could see they were fairly straight, but not as regular as the ones his brother was making.

Summer on the farm always seemed to come with a rush, Joe thought. And it brought plenty of work. There was so much work that Joe and his younger brother didn't have time to go fishing or swimming nearly as often as they would have liked. The vegetable garden had to be planted and hoed. The fruit had to be picked, the hay cut and stacked, the fences mended and the corn hoed to get rid of the weeds. Always before and after every day's work there were the chores of caring for the animals.

In late summer it was time to harvest the wheat.

"Why don't you get one of those new reapers, that the horses can pull?" Joe asked his father.

His father looked up from sharpening the scythe, a curved blade with a long handle. "They cost more than a hundred dollars," he said. "And I figured I didn't need one that much when I had so many strong arms here at home."

The wheat was cut by *cradling*. The cradle was an arrangement of strong slender pieces of wood fastened on the blade of the scythe. This caught the wheat as it was cut. After each long sweep of the blade the stalks of wheat were dumped on the ground. Then it was somebody's job to gather the wheat into bundles and tie the bundles with handfuls of wheat stalks. Another worker followed to set the bundles into shocks. There was quite a trick to this as the bundles or sheaves had to be set so their stem ends were down, and a sheaf had to be spread out over the top to shed water in case of rain.

Joe was proud of the shocks he made. He felt sure no sudden wind would blow them over and scatter the wheat.

Several weeks later when the hot sun had dried the wheat sufficiently, Joe and his brother came along with the wagon. They picked up the bundles with wooden pitchforks and piled them onto the wagon. Then the wagon was driven to a central place on the farm and the wheat was put into a big pile or stack. This, too, had to be shaped a certain way so it was water- and wind-proof. Not everybody could top a stack as well as his father, Joe thought proudly, as he watched the big stack nearing completion.

The threshing was done with a machine called a groundhog. It didn't belong to Joe's father, but to a man who went around to a number of farms one after another and threshed the grain from the stacks. The groundhog was powered by eight horses that belonged to the owner of the machine.

It was a noisy thing that groaned and rattled, but it did thresh the wheat. It was a lot better, Joe thought, than having to beat the grain from the straw with flails on the threshing floor as his grandfather had done. Besides, it was fine having the threshing crew at the farm. It was like having company. His mother and sister cooked extra good meals for the hungry men, with plenty of pies and cakes and all kinds of pickles and preserves.

With the threshing over and the summer ended, it was time to

138

plant the winter wheat, and soon to husk the corn. And then there was school again with a new grade for Joe and more lessons.

Fifty years later, in 1908, and six years before the start of World War I, Joe's grandson, Billy, was living on the same farm where Joe had lived. Many tasks on the farm were still the same. There were the chores night and morning, the feeding of the animals and the milking. There was still winter wheat to be planted, and corn and oats in the spring. Both the wheat and corn were planted by machines pulled by horses, with a man riding on the seat of the machine. There were iron discs and harrows to smooth the fields after plowing. When the corn was a few inches high it was *cultivated* with a plow that had several blades. The blades were set so they straddled the rows of corn. A man rode this cultivator, which was on wheels.

Instead of cradling the wheat, it was harvested with a *reaper*. This was a heavy machine pulled by two, or sometimes three or four horses. The reaper cut the wheat and tied it into bundles with string, called binder twine. It came in big balls about nine inches across and fitted onto a spindle on the binder. The tied bundles of wheat dropped off the reaper onto the ground where a man set them into shocks as Joe had done in his day.

The shocks were left standing in the field until the day the thresher came. The thresher was much bigger than it had been in Billy's grandfather's day. It was called a *separator* because it separated the grain from the straw and chaff. It was pulled by a steam engine. As the engine puffed and wheezed down the road at about three miles an hour every boy in the countryside came running to follow alongside and admire.

All year long Billy waited for the day in late summer when the thresher and its crew would come to his house. Long before the day arrived Billy and his father had gone to the coal mine and brought back a load of coal for the hungry engine. The coal was put in a pile in the feed lot where the threshing machine would stand. Billy went out and looked at the coal every day or so, just to be sure it was still there.

Finally the big day came. The steam engine whistled at their front

Top, 1837 plow; middle left, steam thresher engine with belt to separator; middle right, small groundhog thresher turned by hand; bottom, early horsepower thresher

An early combine (reaper and harvester)

gate and turned into the feed lot. Several neighboring farmers followed with their teams and wagons. They were exchanging work with Billy's father, who had helped on their farms at threshing time.

The engine pulled the separator to the place where Billy's father wanted the straw pile. Then the engine backed off about 50 feet, and stopped, facing the separator. Four men lifted a long leather belt and slipped it over the flywheel of the engine. Then they put the other end loop of the belt around a wide-rimmed wheel on the separator. The belt had to be tight, or it would slip and the separator wouldn't run. This turning belt was the means of transferring the power of the steam engine to the machinery of the separator.

"It's a ticklish business getting the engine set just right," Billy's father explained. "If it's out of line only a little it will throw that heavy belt off the flywheels."

Finally the engineer pulled the whistle cord for a couple of short toots, and the machinery began to turn. A wagon began unloading the sheaves of wheat into the separator, and the yellow straw started shooting out the long pipe at the rear. Soon the golden wheat was pouring out of the side of the separator into a wagon.

Billy's father climbed up and dug his hand into the pile of grain. "That's good wheat, with nice plump kernels. And no weed seeds," he said.

141

After Billy had started driving the horse and buggy to high school, he often thought back to those summers when the threshing was the big part of his year. One summer stood out above all the others. That was the year there had been a friendly engineer in charge of the big steam engine. He had let Billy climb into the engine cab with him. And once he had even let Billy handle the throttle to start the threshing.

"Pull it back slow," the engineer had warned. "If you get in a hurry you can flip that belt off as easy as pie," he said.

Billy moved the throttle handle back slowly and steadily. The big belt began to move and the separator groaned into motion. Men began pitching sheaves of wheat onto the moving platform that led to the cutting knives, and another day's threshing had begun.

For all the machinery in the separator and the power of the steam engine, much horsepower as well as manpower was still needed in the threshing. Horses pulled the wagons that picked up the sheaves from the field. And horses pulled the grain wagon that carried the wheat. At the granary the driver scooped the wheat from the wagon to the storage bin with a big wide shovel while another wagon and team collected wheat at the separator.

There were 25 million horses in the United States at the start of World War I. This meant that it took one quarter of the harvested grain *just to feed the horses.*

Billy thought the methods on his father's farm were quite modern. He thought of the farming that his grandfather had done as being hopelessly old-fashioned. However, by the end of World War II, the American farm had changed again. By the time Billy had reached middle age, the big steam engines were no longer wheezing along the country road. The only place Billy could see one was in a scrap pile or a museum.

The steam engine and the separator had been replaced by an even more efficient machine. Other changes on the farms were just as startling. Lucky for all of us that there were these changes. If they had not occurred, our life as we know it today in this country might not be possible.

CHAPTER 15

MACHINES INVADE THE FARM

If you should go to Indiana you could visit the farm where Joe once lived, and later, his grandson Billy. The land is the same, but nearly everything else about the farm has changed. The sugar maple grove was gone long ago, as well as many of the other trees. Billy and his people are gone, too. Neither he nor any of his family live on the "old home place," as they call the farm. They all have jobs in the city. Strangers are on the farm now, with strange new ways.

To an old-timer like Billy, one of the queerest things about the farm today is the absence of horses. Instead of the horse and buggy that took Billy to high school, there is an automobile. It is sitting in the granary, which has changed its name to the garage. A pickup truck is parked where the wagon used to be. The old barn has been remodeled into a machinery building. A tractor is sitting in front of it, and another one is inside.

Physically, the farm is the same size as it was formerly, about 200 acres. However, the new people rent more land as well.

"A family can't make a living on a small place any more," they say.

Billy shakes his head; but he knows that changes just as radical as this have been taking place all over the United States. In fact, the changes are so great that the experts speak of them as the *second agricultural revolution.*

This revolution, like the first one at Jarmo, did not happen all at once. It was a gradual change that began in the time of Joe's grandfather.

In his grandfather's time all the grain was threshed by men with flails. Using one of these long sticks with the heavy beater-stick fastened on the end, it took a man 10 hours of hard work to beat out seven or eight bushels of wheat. Many inventors were trying to produce a machine that could do this work. By Joe's time they had made one that could thresh wheat and other small grains. It was a crude machine by today's standards but it was better than working with a flail. Of course, it took four men to run the machine and eight horses to furnish the power. They could thresh 300 bushels a day, if the machine didn't break down. Horses were also being used to pull the first crude reapers. By Billy's time steam was doing the threshing, but horses were powering the reaping, planting, cultivating and haying.

As late as 1910 the whole country was still horse-minded. Farmers rode in buggies pulled by horses to towns all over the United States on Saturday afternoons. They tied the horses to hitching racks and went into the stores to do their marketing. Every small town had at least two livery stables where horses and carriages could be stabled or rented — the drive-yourself companies of that day. The sound of horses clop-clopping along the streets could be heard day and night. Many horses shied, and sometimes ran away in fright, at the occasional automobile-monster in their midst.

Ten years later there were nearly as many autos as horses; and by ten more years, the horses and buggies were getting scarce.

Looking back, we can see the change has been truly remarkable. Between 1850 and 1960 there has been more advance in agricultural methods than in the previous 5,000 years. If an early Egyptian farmer of 3,000 years before Christ could have visited Joe's grandfather's farm, he would have seen little to surprise him. If he were to come back today, he would surely think he was in a different world.

Even 50 years ago, in Billy's youth, a man had to invest 106 hours of work to produce 100 bushels of wheat, more than an hour's work per bushel. In 1960, the average for the U.S. was 23 hours for 100 bushels. In this country, one man can produce more than four times the amount of wheat his grandfather did, with the same amount of work.

Gasoline or diesel tractors supply power for hundreds of different farm machines. Power from tractors can be used to dig postholes, saw wood or load feed. This power multiplies by many times the amount of work one man can do in a day. Where the man with a team of horses plowed one furrow at a time, the tractor pulls a set of plows that break four to ten times this amount of ground. Similarly, a tractor may pull several seed drills for planting wheat — each drill seeding and covering a strip of ground ten to twelve feet wide. Formerly, the man driving a team of horses operated one drill which would cover only a width of six feet. Then, too, the tractor works at a speed that is two or three times the rate of the plodding horses.

There are hundreds of other farm machines run by gasoline or diesel power. Few farmers now husk their corn by hand because they use a machine called a corn picker. Migrant laborers, with their long trailing sacks, are being pushed out of the cotton fields by machine cotton pickers. There are machines to dig, sort and sack potatoes. Others are used to spread fertilizer, spray crops, dig and trim radishes and carrots, shake fruit and nuts off trees, cut and bale hay, and pick up nuts from the ground. There is a machine that digs sugar beets, cuts off the tops, takes off most of the dirt and drops them into a truck. Another machine has rubber-covered fingers that vibrate to shake blueberries off the bushes.

The combine harvester, which replaced the steam threshing machine that Billy loved, has many forms and many uses. It received its name because it combines reaping and threshing into one operation.

Some of the combines can cut a swath 20 feet wide as they roll slowly over the huge wheat fields of the United States and Canada. The straw pours out behind in a yellow shower, and the clean, golden-brown kernels of wheat fall into a tank. At intervals the

combine stops to meet a truck which has been parked and waiting at the side of the field. The combine operator pushes a lever, and a stream of wheat pours from a pipe into the truck. Then the truck goes to the elevator or storage bins, and the combine rolls on to harvest more of the golden grain standing ripe and waiting in the sun.

Smaller combines may be pulled by tractors, but the big ones have their own motor power. Combines can be modified so that they harvest such varied crops as corn, beans, sunflower and safflower seeds, rye, oats, flax, rice and many others.

All this machinery means that one man can do the work formerly done by many. For example, the mechanical cotton picker replaces 30 or 40 hand pickers. In mechanized countries this leaves men free to work in other industries besides farming. In Colonial times 85 percent of our population lived on farms. Now only 12 percent do. Even with the methods of Joe's day it would be impossible to feed our expanded population. Nobody wants to go back to the old ways, but we couldn't go back even if we wanted to. Experts predict that the revolution isn't finished, and we can expect to see more and more changes.

One of the newest tools on the farm is the airplane. All of the rice in California, and much of it in Texas and other states, is now planted from planes. Powerful big machines plow and level the ground and dike it to hold water. Then it's flooded with water and heavy wet rice is scattered into the water from a seeder plane. Fertilizer is also spread on the crop by a plane. If weeds come up in the rice, another plane scatters a selective chemical that kills the weeds but leaves the rice unharmed. Still another plane may be used to drive hungry ducks away from the ripening rice. Other crops such as clover and barley are sometimes seeded by planes.

Many planes are used in agriculture to scatter poisons to kill insects attacking the crops. As early as 1925 one company had a fleet of planes to scatter dust on cotton fields to combat the boll weevil, an insect that infests the cotton plant. The planes came to be known as "puffers" because they left a white puffy trail of the dust behind them. Another company makes a plane which they call the "Ag-cat."

Usually agricultural planes don't belong to individual farmers. Special agricultural aviation companies own the planes and hire the pilots. These pilots are known as "crop dusters." They are among the most skillful pilots in the country, since this kind of flying is an exceedingly dangerous occupation. One reason is that crop dusters must fly so close to the ground.

As one company executive said of the pilots, "These boys have to be good or they wouldn't last long."

Another outgrowth of the use of machinery in agriculture is increasing specialization. The farmer of Joe's day raised nearly everything his family needed. Even in Billy's youth the farmer in the Mid-Central states commonly raised a few hogs, kept a small flock of sheep so he could sell the wool and lambs, planted wheat, oats, and corn, raised some chickens, and had a couple of cows to supply him and his family with milk and butter. Many of today's farmers are specialists with bigger farms but fewer crops. Some of these specialty farms are truly remarkable.

Stock is raised by one specialist and fattened for market by another. One farmer in Illinois has 1,000 acres which he plants with corn, alfalfa and pasture. He buys 25,000 calves a year and feeds them until they are ready to sell for beef. Everything on his farm is mechanized. The feed is prepared scientifically by adding just the right amounts of nutrients and vitamins. The mixing of the feed is done automatically by a man who sits in front of a control panel.

A farming family in California is in the rice business. They plant 10,000 acres of rice each year and process it in their own huge dryer and in their rice mill.

Chicken ranchers buy their baby chicks from hatcheries by the thousands and feed them for marketing or keep them for laying. One poultry "factory" may feed and raise many thousands of chickens a year. Turkey ranches are operated in the same manner.

One farmer specialist near Salinas, California, might be called a lettuce king. His farming business includes 6,000 acres of lettuce each year. Much of his land is planted twice and so grows two crops. His operations are carried on in three different climate areas, Central California, Southern California and Arizona, so that from one or the other of them he can pick lettuce every week in the year. Altogether he harvests more than 10,000 carloads of lettuce, which sells for ten to fifteen million dollars. Besides this he raises carrots, broccoli and other vegetable crops, as well as cotton.

To harvest this enormous amount of crops he designed huge machines that creep over the fields like mobile packinghouses. Work-

Tractor breaks up clods.

ing ahead of the machine is a gang of cutters, who cut out the mature lettuce and trim it. Another worker places the heads of lettuce on a moving belt, from which six girls pick them up and wrap them in plastic. They are then sent through an oven that shrinks the plastic to a tight fit, without wilting the lettuce. After this they are packed and boxed by men also riding on the machine.

Next the heads of lettuce are place in crates and chilled in a giant vacuum tube that sucks the air from inside the plastic and chills the lettuce at the same time. Huge forklifts put them in railroad cars where they are shipped all over the United States and Canada. One carload even went to Sweden last year via the Panama Canal. It arrived with the lettuce still crisp and fresh.

The carrot machine is even bigger than the lettuce one. Imagine your house set on wheels moving across a field, processing carrots. On the way, the carrots are washed through three tanks of water, then sprayed with clear water. After this they are moved on an endless belt past 40 girls who select the carrots by grade and size, and pack them in bags.

These millions of dollars' worth of vegetables are all sold to wholesale merchants by telephone. Three salesmen wearing headphones talk all day to buyers in cities all over the country. Their telephone bill is $10,000 a month.

Celery harvester travels five or six feet a minute, covers 24 rows. Celery is cut, trimmed, washed, sorted and packed in crates before it leaves the field harvester.

Working under the owner-head of this incorporated farm, are many managers. Most of them were formerly independent farmers, the lettuce king says. Now as a team they produce more food at less cost, he claims.

This man is not unique in our farming production today. He is typical of the latest trend in mechanization and organization as applied to farming. There are other big producers of vegetables as well as other foods.

All of them, big or small, use more mechanical power than was dreamed of 100 or even 50 years ago. Altogether they raise more food than the world ever had before. Unfortunately, the world's transportation facilities, such as trains, ships and planes, haven't improved as much as crop production. Neither has the ability of hungry peoples to buy these extra crops. This leaves some countries with surplus foods — more than they need to feed their people — and other countries with too little. The surplus foods have to be stored, and many have to be fumigated to kill insects that attack them. This is an expensive process. In 1959 the United States spent 205 million dollars to store surplus wheat. For the period between June 30, 1961, and June 30, 1962, the cost was over 156 million dollars. In 1963 the United States made plans to sell 150 million bushels of surplus wheat to the Soviet Union.

Mechanization is only part of the hope for the hungry people of the world. Mechanization alone would not help the farmer in Indonesia who farms less than an acre of ground. Our farmers in the United States were in a position to profit from this power development because the farms in the United States have always been relatively large compared to most other countries.

In this country we are fortunate to be able to get this abundant food from the plants of the earth. As we continue to work, perhaps it will be possible to share more and more of it with the hungry people of the world.

CHAPTER 16

PLANTS AND SPACESHIPS

Suppose you were chosen as one of the passengers for a long trip in a spaceship. What things would you and your fellow travelers need to take along on the trip? Would you pack special clothes and foods? What about air to breathe? You are going to need all of these. Also, if you don't include some plants in your preparations, you will be in serious trouble.

In May of 1962 there was an important meeting of space scientists in Dayton, Ohio. Experts from all over the United States presented talks about their experiments on the development of space systems.

There were disagreements among the scientists, but not about one thing. They all agreed that if rocket travelers are to go on long trips into outer space, or stay more than a month on the surface of the moon, there is only one way to make this possible. This is by integrating some kind of green plant into the space system.

Space travelers going on a relatively short trip, say to the moon and back, can carry all they need of food, water and air to breathe, the scientists pointed out. However, the length of time they can stay on the moon is definitely limited by the amount of these necessities they can take along. Suppose, for instance, that 100 men wanted to

Artist's concept of a lunar excursion module carrying two astronauts to the moon's surface.

stay on the moon for as long as a year. How much food, oxygen and water would they need?

The average adult eats about two and a half to three pounds of food per day. This weight includes a large amount of water that is in many foods. Even if the foods were dehydrated so that their weight was cut to one pound per day, more than 18 *tons* of food would be required for the hundred men. Add to this the amount of water needed by the moon dwellers (roughly four pounds per man per day) and the oxygen for breathing (two pounds per day). The total weight that must be carried is staggering. The number of rockets needed to carry such an amount of materials would be more than any country could furnish. A trip to one of the planets would take even more supplies.

Therefore, say the scientists, if man wants to travel for long distances in space he must carry along the *same kind of supply system he has here on earth.* In other words, he must take along green plants which not only supply oxygen as it is used up by the people and animals, but manufacture all the food in the world which our animals — and hence people — need for energy.

Many laboratories have been studying green algae as a source of food for man, since these plants not only furnish carbohydrates and vitamins, but also considerable amounts of protein. They have also been using them in many trial space systems. One laboratory built a space unit that would support one man. In it they put enough glass tanks of green algae to give off enough oxygen for the man to breathe.

A small room in the shape of a cylinder, five feet in diameter and seven feet long, was made for the space traveler. Energy for the algae's photosynthesis was furnished by 250 square feet of fluorescent lights. This is about as many lights as would cover one wall of a good-sized living room. In front of these lights were thin plexiglass tanks holding about 100 gallons of water and algae. Since the lamps and algae tanks were sandwiched together in layers, they could be put in a relatively small space.

The air from this space room was forced through the tanks of algae where it lost some of its carbon dioxide (produced by the breathing man) and gained some oxygen. Then it was dried of excess water and sent back to the room.

Several trial "trips" were made in this space room. None of them, of course, ever left the building, since the room was not built into a rocket as yet. The longest "trip" lasted three days and two nights. During this time a man lived in the small space room and received no other air or oxygen than that produced by the growing algae.

One scientist conjectured how such a system could be used on the moon. He pointed out that only at the moon's poles would there be any continuous sunshine. Other parts would be in sunlight for only about 13 earth days. These would be followed by an equal number of days of darkness. At the poles where there would be sunlight, there might also be serious bombardment by falling meteors, similar to the ones that in the past have made the deep craters in the moon's surface. He suggested that the space station might have to be placed underground. If lights were used instead of sunshine to furnish the energy for the plant's photosynthesis, then some form of power would have to be provided in the space station to run the lamps.

Other scientists discussed the possibility of a plant system that would supply not only oxygen for breathing but also most of the food for the space travelers. One mentioned the experiments in which food for man has been made from green algae, but suggested

Interior for 3-man Apollo spacecraft. Astronauts wear light coveralls. Pressure suit can be donned quickly in an emergency.

that perhaps other forms of plants would be tastier. While mice fed on tablets made from green algae remain in good health, the same algae as food for men is not very palatable.

It would be better, he said, to have a complete food cycle such as is found on earth. In this, the simple plants such as algae or lichens would manufacture food by means of photosynthesis. These plants would be fed to animals. Men would then eat the animals, as well as other higher plants which they would grow at the space station. The waste products from the men and animals would be broken down by bacteria and fungi so they could in turn be used to supply needed chemicals for the plants.

This scientist figured that five acres of plants would supply food for 100 men at the moon station, if animals also were raised for protein. He added that some supplies would have to be brought from earth. No simulated "trip" of this kind of system has been made but one will have to be tried before too long.

The first lunar landing will mark the end of the beginning of the space age, Dr. J. C. Finn, Jr., North American Aviation Company scientist, said at the May meeting. He estimated that somewhere be-

Artist's concept of lunar excursion module after moon landing. One astronaut explores moon landscape. One astronaut will always stay in module during exploration.

tween three and ten years after the first landing a lunar base will be needed. If space exploration goes as scheduled, the first lunar base would be established about 1975. Perhaps one of you reading this book will be among the people in that lunar station.

Before this time many studies have to be made, and much information gathered. Space units have to be built and tested. Plant systems have to be constructed that can be trusted to last indefinitely and supply the needs of men. All this study takes time.

People have done a great deal with plants in the past as well as recently. They have cultivated the desirable ones for food and many other uses. They have tried to suppress the ones that seemed to be harmful. However, they have never had to worry about keeping plants alive so there would be air to breathe. The plants have been doing this automatically. This is the nature of plants. The system of balance between plants and animals on this earth was stable long before man appeared on the earth.

As Dr. Finn said in the space meeting, "Green plants — both higher and lower forms — stand between man and his extinction."

156

INDEX

158

160